ROBOTS AT WORK

A practical guide
for engineers and managers

John Hartley

IFS (Publications) Ltd, UK
North-Holland Publishing Company
1983

ISBN 0-903608-34-0
ISBN 0444-86638 8

Publishers:
IFS (Publications) Ltd.
35-39 High Street, Kempston, Bedford, M K42 7BT, U K
and
North-Holland Publishing Company
Amsterdam · New York · Oxford

Typesetting by Fleetlines Typesetters, Southend-on-Sea, England.
Printed by Anchor Press Ltd., Colchester, England.

Acknowledgement

I SHOULD LIKE to thank all those who have made this book possible, especially the many people who have shown me the robots they have developed, or their robots in action.

Then I should like to thank John Mortimer, managing director IFS (Publications) Ltd, who as the Editor of *The Engineer*, first encouraged me to follow the robot scene.

I should also like to thank the following companies for illustrations: ASEA, British Leyland, Cloos, Fanuc, Fiat, Ford, GEC, General Motors, Hitachi, Kawasaki Heavy Industries, Kobe Steel, KUKA, Mitsubishi Electric, Mitsubishi Heavy Industries, Murata Manufacture, Nissan Motors, Nitto Seiki, Renault, Saab-Scania, Shin Meiwa, Sumitomo Electric, Unimation and Yaskawa.

I should also like to thank IFS (Publications) Ltd, for permission to use many illustrations from their conference proceedings and magazines, such as *The Industrial Robot, Assembly Automation* and *Sensor Review*. Also my thanks are due to the Japan Industrial Robot Association for permission to use a number of illustrations from the proceedings of the 11th International Symposium on Industrial Robots and *Robots* quarterly journal.

Contents

Preface

INDUSTRIAL robots are leading us into a revolution in working, and in the way that factories are run. Yet to many managers robots are too expensive and too complicated. To employees, robots seem a threat.

In this book, I have tried to show, therefore, which robots can be used successfully where, and how some manufacturers are already doing so – profitably. Not every robot is suitable for every job, so the reasons why different types are selected, and the actual results being achieved with robots by many different companies are covered. Many of these case studies show the use of Japanese factories, because it is in Japan that the robot has been most exploited, and most successfully. I have also taken a glimpse at the effects on employment and working practices, short and long term developments.

But there is no doubt the use of robots will be the key to growth in manufacture in the next decade, for both large and small companies, and my hope is that this book will encourage more companies to use robots to boost productivity.

Of course, expensive mistakes can be made, but the way to find out how to use robots is to install a couple of machines and see how they perform. One reason for doing so is that the robot has an inheritent guarantee: if it does not pay in one job, you can move it somewhere else, learning as you do so. In the end, robots are limited more by the imagination of production engineers and managers than anything else, so now is the time to expand that imagination and reap the rewards.

CHAPTER ONE

Why robots?

ARE robots the key to high productivity with flexibility? Will they be the cause of massive unemployment, or will their use lead to a new world in which people are spared the drudgery of repetitive or dangerous work so that they can turn their abilities to more appealing work?

These may seem imponderable questions at present, but it is already clear that the industrial robot will be used in such great numbers in the coming decade that no one in industry can afford to ignore them – be he manager, technician, assembly worker or unionist. Unfortunately, owing to the robot's apparent affinity with slaves of evil forces from outer space, it has often been sensationalised in such a way that many people think it a threat without knowing what it is.

Yet the reality is that at present, anyway, the robot is merely a dumb machine that gives the manufacturer more flexibility than other forms of automation – but at a price. That price, which is not merely monetary, is changing all the time. Over the last twenty years, the cost of a universal robot has hardly increased, yet labour costs have quadrupled. In 1981, Unimation Inc claimed that the hourly cost of a robot was about 30% of labour costs in the US automotive industry, whereas in 1966 the costs were similar. Clearly, the balance has already moved so far that the proliferation of robots is inevitable. (Figs. 1.1, 1.2, 1.3.)

Robots are generally shown as devices with one or more arms making motions like humans. Since that was the form of the earliest robots, it is not unreasonable, but we are now moving into an era where robots will not necessarily be recognisable by shape – some may look like trolleys, others will be machines in boxes, while others may look more like a human being, with two arms, and some form of forward motion. What distinguishes a

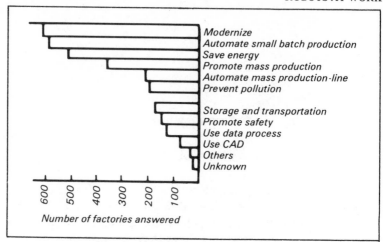

Number of factories answered

Fig 1.1   The motivation for investment

robot from other pieces of equipment is the way it is controlled, and the wide range of things it can do, not its appearance.

The questions now facing industry are: Do we use robots? Where do we use them? What type should we use? What will be the advantages, and how will they affect the workforce? Even in the future, the robot will not be the solution for every manufacturing problem, despite the fact that its use will spread to applications outside manufacture, and the numbers in use will increase dramatically.

The principle advantage of the robot is its flexibility: it can

Fig 1.2   The main advantages of robots

Improvement in productivity through the use of robots	94.0%
Stabilisation of product quality and improved job efficiency	69.7%
Improved labour safety	52.8%
Changing workers' attitudes	51.4%
Shortage of labourer and skilled worker	45.0%
Increased flexibility of production system	39.7%
Progress of engineering and technology of robot	37.3%

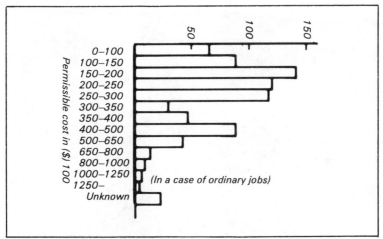

Fig 1.3   Permissible amount of money for investment in robot equivalent to an operator

cope with different products on one line, as market demand changes; it can be re-programmed to suit minor modifications or when a completely new model is introduced. Thus, it offers the high-volume manufacturer a way of coping with change in volume or type; and the small manufacturer the chance of a big jump in productivity while continuing to produce in small batches, such that in some cases he may be able to compete with much larger companies.

For example, one of the biggest applications of robots is in spot welding of car bodies. This is repetitive work, with the same welds being done on up to 1,000 bodies a day for four or five years without change. That does not sound a good use of robots, but it has turned out to be very common. Of course, the job can be done by multiwelders, but in that case, any late changes to the design of the car result in delays before production can start and extra cost. With robots, the design can be changed at the last minute without any problems. In addition, with multiwelders, it is normally necessary for one line of machines to be installed for each body type; with robots, one line can handle many different models. Finally, when the body is replaced by a new design, the robots can carry on in use. Of course, the ultimate in flexibility is a human being, for whom that work is tiring and tedious. He has to bend awkwardly carrying a heavy welding gun, and has to try to space the spot welds equally

Fig 1.4   Robot welding is the job that people do not want to do

along the body flanges at a high speed. Therefore, it is a job that most people do not want to do. (Fig. 1.4)

Often, the robot is seen as a rival to the worker, but in reality it is the rival of other forms of automation – called 'hard automation' or 'dedicated machinery'. The reason for this is that the trend is to increased automation in industry whether robots are used or not. To increase competitiveness industry must increase productivity and the quality of its products; there is no alternative. Cheap labour is abundant in many countries that are hungry to industrialise, and this pattern of newly industrialised nations taking over the manufacture of low-technology products will continue. However, as time goes on, so these countries want higher levels of technology, so there will be more and more competition for industries in developed nations. In that battle to increase productivity while maintaining the flexibility needed to react to forces of the market and competition, there is no doubt that the industrial robot is a valuable tool.

But what do we mean by industrial robot? There are many definitions, but the one adopted by most societies concerned with robots are broadly in line; the odd man out is Japan, where almost anything that has some handling function is called a robot. As far as industry is concerned, a robot is something that can carry out a variety of functions. It is something that can be used to do one job one day, and another the next, without any hardware being changed. Thus, a simple arm used to load and unload at a machine cannot really be called a robot unless it can be reprogrammed to do a different job. If it is necessary for an operator to physically change something like a limit stop, then that is no robot. In fact, in the Japanese definition, such devices are considered to be robots, which means that thousands of robots have been in use in industry everywhere for decades. (Fig. 1.5)

So, by robot, we mean a numerically controlled (NC) or playback robot. This means that the robot can be programmed to carry out one or many tasks, and can subsequently be switched from one job to another at the touch of a button, or by an electric signal, or by being reprogrammed. For example, in the case of a spray painting robot, the operator normally programmes the machine by moving the robot arm and spray gun through the motions he would use to spray the workpiece himself. He could programme the robot to spray six or eight

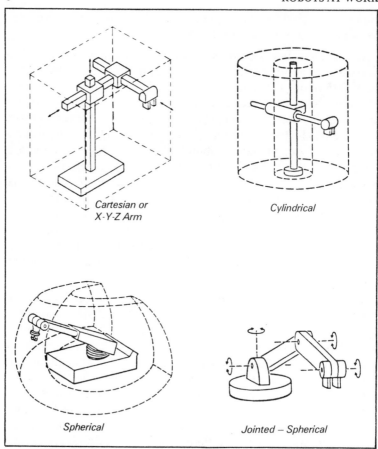

Fig 1.5   Four main configurations of robot that are currently in use

parts. When the machine starts work, the operator can leave it to spray a batch of parts, and then change the program to suit a new batch, or a control system can be set up so that the robot can recognise the parts as they come, and change the program accordingly.

To meet this definition, the robot does not necessarily need an electronic control system, since it is possible for pneumatic valves to give such flexibility. Nor does it need to be a highly complex device with all manner of sensors. Just as there are skilled and unskilled workers, so there are robots with different levels of capability.

But robot definitions were established in the days of 'general purpose' robots, when one design was produced for welding, handling and painting. Thus, the definitions tend to revolve around arms of various types. However, such a definition is now too narrow. The key to the flexible operation of a robotic device is its controller, and electronics are developing so rapidly that such controllers can be used economically in many machines. Thus, it seems logical to include as robots any devices that have the flexibility of the universal robot.

For example, an assembly robot might look just like a handling robot, the only difference being the accuracy with which it can position its gripper. On the other hand, it might be completely different, consisting of a number of delivery chutes, and moving columns to do the assembly. A welding robot may be a universal robot, or it may look like a standard welding machine with an electronically controlled moving work table. Then, a handling robot may be a jointed arm, or an unmanned trolley with automatic loading and unloading devices. On the other hand, a trolley that runs up and down rails, between fixed points, and has automatic loading/unloading devices for certain specific products is normally a piece of hard automation.

Of course, these definitions are irrelevant to the factory manager who is merely looking for a flexible device to do a certain job. But it is important to realise that to have the capability of a robot, a machine does not need to look like a Dalek. At present, this is not so much a problem, except that some companies are busy tying 'robot' labels on ordinary machines in the hope of boosting sales. But in the future, as the concept of flexible manufacture develops, it is essential not to be too rigid with definitions.

In the early days, robots were essentially arms designed to duplicate human movements. Thus, there was usually a rotating base, carrying a column with telescopic arm, or a jointed arm. The 'wrist' could be rotated and bent. Initially, these robots were very costly, so it was uneconomic to use them for simple jobs like handling. In fact, as mentioned earlier, one of the earliest applications to find widespread use was in the spot welding of car bodies. This was also the application that aroused the most publicity because 10 to 30 robots were usually placed in line to do the job – in most other jobs, such as spray painting or arc welding, only a few were used in one shop, so the effect was not dramatic.

It soon became clear that the robot welders were not only giving greater flexibility than multiwelders, but their 'downtime' – the time when the machine is not actually working – was far less. The reason was simple: if a multiwelder stops, the whole production line stops; if one robot stops working, its job can be done either by a spare robot or by a standby human welder while the robot is being repaired. In addition, because the robot always puts the spot welds in the same position the quality was far better than with manual welding. As a result, it was found that the number of welds could be reduced, giving a further gain in productivity. This 'robot bonus' – an unlooked for benefit – is found in most robot applications.

Of course, the use of robots for spot welding of car bodies seems suited only to large companies, but most other robot applications are ideal for small companies. Indeed, the robot is the small company's route to automation, quite simply because hard automation is too expensive and too inflexible. Large companies often find hard automation a more economic solution than robots. For example, one of Nissan Motor Co's large and modern plants produces 130,000 transmissions and 130,000 steering gears each month, with 4,700 people. To gain high productivity, handling at virtually all the machine tools is automated and there is an extensive system of conveyors and buffer stores for partly-machined gears and shafts.

Included in the automation are some 1,500 automatic parts loading devices. These are not robots, but arms and grippers carried on gantries to load and unload shafts and gears. It is true that the same basic design is used at all machines, the gripper and movements only differing from machine to machine, but these devices do not have the flexibility of robots and are of a type widely used in industry. Each can move only from one position to another and back again in one sequence. They are used in conjunction with a very complex and costly conveyor system to give fully automatic handling, which is ideal for a large company with high volume production, but would be prohibitively expensive for a small company – and for quite a few relatively large ones as well. (Fig. 1.6)

That is where the robot comes in. For example, a small company making concrete drill bits decided to set up a new machine shop and opted for 14 NC machines served by 11 robots supplemented by bar auto turret lathes. The result was

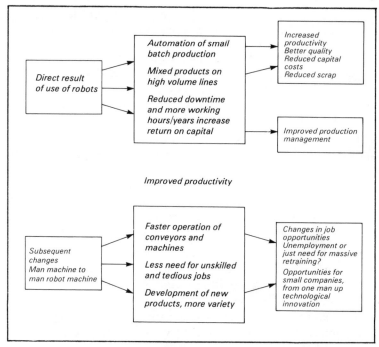

Fig 1.6 A chart to show the effects of introducing robots

that 25 people were needed instead of 100, and only 14 of these are direct labour. The point is that with the robots, high productivity is available without the addition of an expensive conveyor system – of course, a conveyor would increase productivity at a cost in terms of flexibility. But without it, the small company can compete with much bigger ones.

✓ And that is the reason why robots will revolutionise manufacture; they will enable the small companies, which are inherently flexible, and often very dynamic, to match the giants in terms of productivity. So, most of the applications for robots are relevant to all companies in manufacture, but especially to the smaller ones.

Spray painting was an early application for robots, mainly because an engineer in a small Norwegian company decided to design a machine to overcome hold-ups in his own spraybooths. Initially, robots were used to spray small components passing through booths, but subsequently, the automotive industry started to use them to apply underseal beneath car bodies. The motivation was that this is a very dirty job, with the operator frequently crouching beneath the body.

Arc welding was the next application, but it took a long time to get going, owing to the cost of the robot, and its inadequacy in following a joint that was not precisely in the expected position – in other words, there was a need for a robot with some ability to see the position of the weld. The robot could deal with thick plates without any vision sensing, but in those applications, the increase in productivity hardly justified the cost. Eventually, it was the in-between welding where robots took hold – the relatively large batches of brackets and sub-assemblies produced by suppliers to the automotive industry. Now, that business is one of the largest growth areas for robots.

At first, it seemed that handling would be a major use of robots, but again, in many applications, the unseeing robot proved to be at a disadvantage. One exception was in handling at machine tools, where the robot could work in a small area, between pre-determined areas, and with relatively few variations in the parts to be handled. Indeed the robot proved to be a key in the development of flexible machining systems intended to operate unmanned at night.

Assembly is clearly the biggest potential application for robots, but again, in the early stages, the opportunities for the use of robots seemed limited. One reason was the inaccuracy of the robot, another was the complicated nature of the task, and another was the need for several different tools. Vision and tactile sensing seemed necessary, but it has now been shown that blind robots, with little special tactile sensing can be used for assembly in many operations. Obviously, the use of tactile and vision sensing expand the applications for robots. Nevertheless, in many assembly operations the robot does not seem to be the answer.

For example, the minimum cycle time – the time required for a complete assembly operation, from picking the part up, to putting it down again – for a robot is about three seconds. Yet many automatic assembly lines are processing parts with cycle times of 2-4s. In addition, the production volumes are so large that the hard automation can be depreciated very rapidly, while variety is small. But as the trend to greater variety gathers way, so robots will find more applications in assembly.

As new uses for robots have developed, so special require-ments not met by existing designs have been discovered. For example, the conventional robot used for body welding is too big and too slow. Therefore, smaller units, which can be grouped together to work at one place, have been developed. Robots have been designed specially for assembly, and others specially for painting, and this trend of robots being developed specially for certain purposes is certain to increase in the future, as demand expands. At the same time, the actual shape of the robot will change. For example, the robots used at machine tools were initially free-standing devices, which could have been used for many other jobs. But now, most are mounted on the machine itself, and their movements have been developed specifically to load and unload workpieces only.

Assembly and inspection are the areas where this change in form can be expected to be most marked. Usually, there are many operations in assembly, and where practical it is logical to design a machine or series of machines that can assemble a part, instead of using a row of robots with a lot of ancillary equip-ment. Where it is not practical, cell assembly, with a group of robots gathered around an assembly table will be preferred. That cell approach could also find its way into the repair shop.

Up to now, managers involved in manufacture have been con-cerned primarily with the machinery, and how it will perform. However, the advent of the industrial robot alters the whole climate in the workshop. Clearly, the demand for labour to carry out unskilled assembly and machine minding tasks will diminish. There will also be less need for skilled welders and paint sprayers and a whole range of skills will appear at first sight to be redundant. At the same time, many more skilled workers able to programme and maintain robots will be needed. With the greater variety in products that is expected, more designers and development engineers will be needed.

At first sight, this would suggest that unemployment of unskilled and semi-skilled workers will increase. In fact, however, it is more likely that the pattern of work will change. First, of course, someone has to produce all the robots needed, while new products are being devised at a great rate. It all means that for every door to employment that closes, another will open, although it will be difficult for the shopfloor worker to recognise that the door exists and how to go through it. Thus, while managers are busy planning how to use their robots, they must also spend a lot of time on retraining their staff. But if these two challenges are accepted at the outset, and tackled positively, the robot offers society a new era.

If it is up to factory managers to handle the problems of how to use robots and their workforce, it is up to society as a whole to decide how to handle some of the more general implications. For example, as productivity and the ability to produce a variety of products increases, there will be a temptation for us to squander our resources such as minerals and oil on useless products. To prevent the robot revolution getting out of hand, a lot of care is needed – perhaps as much in this respect as in the case of unemployment.

CHAPTER TWO

Robot types – evolution from a universal position

INITIALLY, robots were seen as the solution to mechanical handling – for loading and unloading at machine tools, injection moulding machines, presses, as well as the beginning and end of assembly lines. Since the robots should be able to place components in sequence in different positions, palletizing was also seen as a potential application. Therefore, the early robots were generally of the universal type, and were designed to carry loads of 10–50kg.

So the question facing robot designers was how to provide movements that would provide maximum coverage in a certain space with rapid, smooth manipulation. Among the early robot designs were the Unimate series and the Versatran, which took different forms that have since become two of the standards. The Unimate 2000 and 4000 models are of the spherical or polar type, in which the gripper can more or less cover the space enclosed by a sphere. (Fig. 2.1)

The main elements of the Unimates are a base and arm. The arm can rotate on the base, usually through 220 to 270°, while the arm can also pivot vertically on a yoke to give up-and-down movement. Then, the arm is telescopic. Therefore, the arm itself can move in three different ways – rotation, tilting and extension. These are called 'three degrees of freedom', or 'three axes of motion' and define the capability of a robot. In addition, the wrist can have up to three degrees of freedom: it can bend in a vertical plane, swivel on a horizontal plane, and rotate on the arm. In all, six degrees of freedom are available, but fewer are often adequate. Therefore, robots are usually designed on a modular basis, so that, for example, a wrist with one, two or three axes of motion can be provided. A critical feature with this or any other robot, is its working envelope. Other robots of the

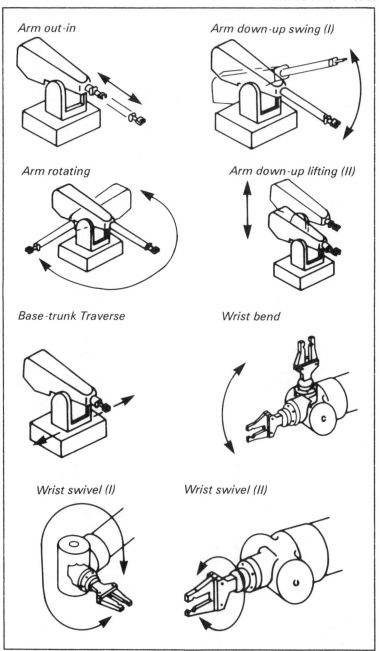

Arm out-in

Arm down-up swing (I)

Arm rotating

Arm down-up lifting (II)

Base-trunk Traverse

Wrist bend

Wrist swivel (I)

Wrist swivel (II)

Fig 2.1   The basic motions of a robot, showing also the wrist
movements

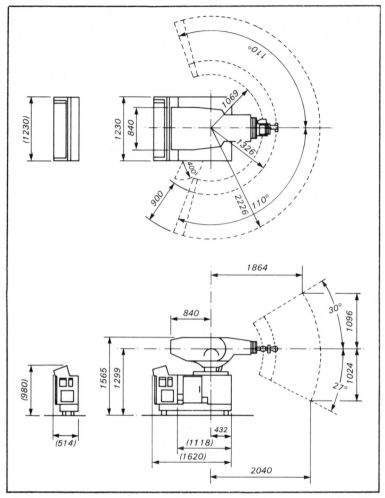

*Fig 2.2   The basic movements covered by the Unimate are also shared
by units from Comau and Volkswagen*

polar type are the Comau Pola, and Volkswagen units. (Fig. 2.2)

The Cartesian co-ordinate robot is one that consists of a
column and arm. It is sometimes called an x-y-z robot, indicating the axes of motion. The x axis is lateral motion, the y axis is
longitudinal motion – that is away and towards the workpiece –
while the z axis is vertical. Thus, the arm can move up and down
on the column, (z axis) which may be able to slide along on its
base (x axis). Then, the arm can telescope (y axis) to move the

gripper horizontally. The gripper may be able to rotate, bend and swivel, but often the Cartesian co-ordinate robot has fewer degrees of freedom than the spherical type. In some cases, the arm hangs down from rails on a gantry, and it can move longitudinally and transversely on the frame – that is in the x and y axes. Robots include the DEA Pragma, Renault Acma Cribier and Mitsubishi Robitus spot welding robots, and the original Shin Meiwa arc welding machines. (Fig. 2.3)

The cylindrical type of robot is a variation on the Cartesian co-ordinate type, and a popular one at that. Typical examples are the Fanuc robots designed for handling machine tools and assembly. These robots also consist of a base and column, but in this case, the column rotates. It carries an extending arm which can move up and down on the column to provide the three basic degrees of freedom.

Fig 2.3.   The Fanuc handling robot is a Cartesian co-ordinate machine

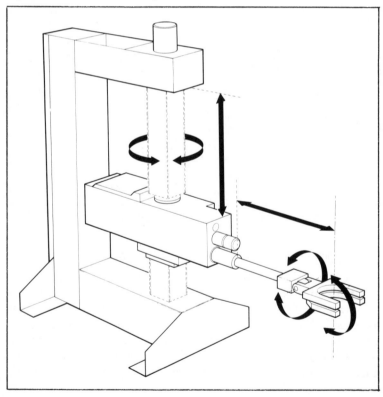

Then, there is the jointed arm robot, which resembles the human arm, although not usually in its free position. It usually stands on a base on which it can rotate, while it can articulate at the 'shoulder' joint which is just above the base. Then, it can articulate about its 'elbow' and 'wrist' joints. With swivelling and bending at the wrist, six degrees of freedom can be obtained. This is probably the most popular form for a robot, the ASEA and KUKA robots being among the early models, as was the Trallfa painting robot, but the Cincinnati Milacron T3, Yaskawa Motoman, Unimation Puma, Hall Automation (now part of GEC) CompArm and Matsushita AW-2000 are among the many of this type in use. Another version of the jointed arm robot is one in which the arm is mounted on its side on a pillar, the shoulder and elbow joint both articulating on vertical axes. This form first appeared as the Scara robot. (Fig.2.4)

But why are some types of robot preferred for some jobs, and what do these different types mean to the user? Of course, the scene is continually changing, and there are overlapping areas, but the advantage of the jointed arm robot is that it can move in complex paths relatively easily, and thus it has become the most popular type for arc welding and spray painting – in fact, it is virtually the only type used for spraying.

Shin Meiwa adopted the Cartesian co-ordinate concept for arc welding, mainly because it was interested in very large assemblies and long cycle times. This type of robot can of course cover a very large area, especially if the robot hangs

Fig 2.4   On some robots two kinds of operation can be selected using software for co-ordinate conversion to achieve straightline welding with all axes

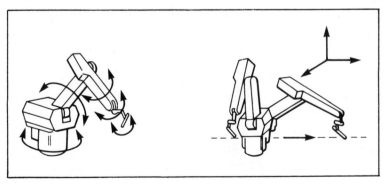

down from a gantry as in the case of the Shin Meiwa design. Indeed, the size of the working area can be several metres in x and y axes. This type of robot has also been adopted for assembly purposes, where there can be one or more arms hanging down over a worktable. Indeed this is an excellent arrangement, since the robot does not occupy any floor space other than the working area. (Fig. 2.5)

The cylindrical type is suitable for big loads, since the column can be very rigid – this also applies to the Cartesian robot – and it can also have a long reach. Also, of course, it is ideal where the gripper has to be moved forwards and backwards horizontally frequently and at high speed – as in loading and unloading machine tools. Like the jointed arm type, it does not need much floor space.

For spot welding, either the jointed arm or polar type is preferred. Many Unimate 2000 and 4000 polar robots are used in spot welding car bodies, although General Motors has used many Cincinnati jointed arm robots. Jack Lane of General Motors Institute in the USA, explained the selection of the jointed arm type for a small truck cab by saying 'due to the many diverse locations of welds, it was determined that the spherical-jointed configuration offered the greatest flexibility in gaining access to the panels.' He said that with other robot types, more difficulty would have been encountered in programming, and a longer cycle time would have been needed.

Some jointed arm robots are designed so that the upper or shoulder joint can pivot through 120°, allowing the arm to pick something up in front of the robot and turn right over to place the part behind it. This design can be very useful in handling, since this motion can usually be accomplished far more quickly than the robot can rotate on a vertical axis to move the part.

Of course, the mechanical form of the robot was only one important aspect of the design. A lot of effort was needed to develop mechanisms that could operate repeatedly to close tolerances. Then, the actuation and control systems had to be reliable, smooth in operation and easy for the operator to programme.

Initially, most of the robots designed to carry loads of 10kg and upwards were actuated hydraulically, whereas some very small robots were actuated pneumatically. With the advent of

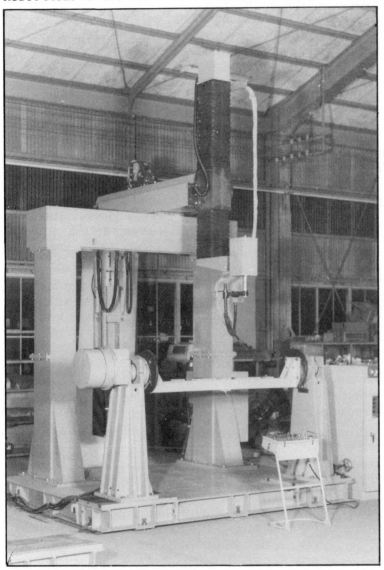

Fig 2.5.   A Shin Meiwa Cartesian co-ordinate machine for arc welding

microprocessor controls, there was a swing towards the use of electric dc servo motors, which had already proved to be reliable and smooth in operation, whereas some of the earlier hydraulically powered machines were rather jerky. Thus, from the outset, electric drives were preferred for arc welding. But since maintenance staff need electrical and mechanical skills whatever the robot, electrically-driven robots have become much more popular than hydraulic ones, for which an extra skill is needed – not that robots require much in-house maintenance. Electrically-driven machines are generally claimed to consume less energy than hydraulic ones, one manufacturer claiming that the energy consumption of his robot is only 15–20% of that of an equivalent hydraulically actuated machine.

Although the all-electric machine would seem to be the robot of the future, there are cases in which a simple pneumatic device is more than adequate. Where the robot is used as a pick-and-place device – and there are literally millions of applications – pneumatics, which are simple and cheap, are ideal. In any case, some pneumatic controllers offer considerable flexibility.

Apart from the simplest units, the robot is a complex combination of precision mechanical engineering and electronics, and there is some controversy whether electronic or mechanical companies are most likely to dominate the robot manufacturing industry by the end of the decade. Many of the latecomers into the business have been companies with experience in both fields. In Japan, for example, Mitsubishi Electric, Hitachi and Matsushita all come into this category, as do GEC in Britain, whereas KUKA of Germany, Comau of Italy and Cincinnati Milacron of the USA are principally mechanical engineering companies.

However, the need for repeatability of ± 1mm for any robot, and ± 0.05–0.1mm for assembly robots, perhaps with compliant grippers, places a considerable burden on the mechanical engineering skills of the manufacturer. Therefore, it is not surprising that machine tool companies, or those with experience of similar products should number among the ranks of robot makers. At the same time, of course, the need to programme a jointed arm robot so that all the axes are actuated simultaneously to move the gripper horizontally involves a considerable understanding of electronics.

Various drive mechanisms are used in robots, but the most popular are ball screws and Harmonic Drive units. The ball screw converts rotary into linear motion. The dc servo motor is mounted at the end of the ball screw, which it rotates, so that the nut moves linearly along the screw. For example, in a jointed

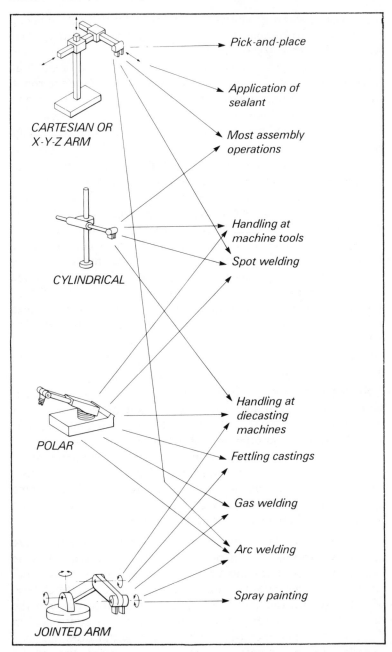

Fig 2.6   The manner in which the four basic types of robot configuration
          are related to various applications in the factory

arm robot, a screw mounted almost vertically behind the robot can be used to actuate the main shoulder joint. A harmonic drive, which consists of an annular gear in which a smaller planetary gear runs – there is no sun gear – gives reduction gearing with great precision. It is often used to rotate the robot on its base, and the forearm about the elbow joint. To provide linear movement along a slide – floor or gantry mounted – or telescopic action of an arm, a ball screw or rack and pinion can be used.

However, Volkswagen uses a toothed belt drive to actuate several axes of its robots, including telescoping of the arm. Precision spiral bevel gears are used at many wrists. Clearly, there is plenty of choice, but where precision is needed, the ball screw/ harmonic drive combination seems to have gained the ascendancy. Of course, it is possible that once certain robot mechanisms become standard they will be made in large volumes by a few specialists so that there will be little difference in the mechanical form and repeatability of robots. If that happens, then it seems certain that the electronics companies will come to dominate the robot business, although Joe Engelberger, president of Unimation, thinks that the mechanisms are complex enough to keep the electronics companies at bay. (Fig. 2.6)

Such thoughts were far from the minds of the people designing, selling and installing early robots. One of the problems of those machines was that the controls were not really flexible enough, while programming was laborious. A variety of controllers were used – some mechanical, some pneumatic, some electric, and some electro-hydraulic. Clearly, some were more flexible than others, but it soon became apparent that in some applications, the ease with which a robot could be programmed or 'taught' could play a major part in selection.

If the robot is rarely reprogrammed, or if the cycle times are very slow, programming is not a problem. But where it may be necessary to reprogramme a robot to do the job of another that has broken down, speed is vital. Normally, there is a 'teach box' with the robot, and the operator takes the robot through the required path to programme it. Most robots are controlled on the 'point-to-point' method, in which the operator does not need to follow the exact path throughout the program. Instead, he moves from point to point, and the controller interpolates the path between the points. To make the robot follow an arc, it is normally necessary to identify three points on that arc only.

The early Cartesian type robots, such as the Shin Meiwa design, took a long time to teach. It was necessary to move the robot through one axis at a time. Thus, to move the gun at 45 deg, the operator moved a little way vertically, then horizontally, and then vertically before reaching the desired spot. In a long program, this could take many minutes. Then, more time would be needed to check and refine the movements. If, as could often be the case, the robot had to be reprogrammed several times a day, the utilisation of the robot could be quite low.

In the early days, therefore, everything was against the robot. The result was that many companies designed robots, and then found that they were uneconomic; others took out a licence or marketing agreement with another manufacturer, but after a while gave up. Of course, many of those companies had jumped into the business with little real knowledge of what was involved. They did not design production systems, nor were they prepared to develop slowly and thoroughly but at a relatively low cost to be ready for the robot revolution. The accountants who controlled such companies were soon able to show the engineers that they were wasting their time. The short-sighted people won, and in many cases, when the time came for a major push into robots, their previous experience led them to ignore this business.

Of course, there were many good reasons for opting out of robots. First, the early machines were very expensive; secondly, as the manufacturers had no experience, they were selling the robots as do-anything universal devices; thirdly, there was the time taken to programme the robot, and there was usually insufficient capacity for enough steps for many different jobs to be stored. Then, once the program was set, it was difficult to change it. In addition, of course, engineers were worried about reliability and the effects of wear on accuracy.

In this period, the one company that kept working away at developing and selling robots was Unimation Inc, formerly a subsidiary of Condec in the USA and now part of Westinghouse. Although Unimation developed excellent products, its manufacture was not systemised. Output increased, but for many years Unimation continued to build robots on a one-by-one basis, so that profits were low, and many teething troubles developed when the machines reached the production lines. Of course, one problem was that salesmen of the early robots tended to make promises that the robots could not fulfil. Another problem was that in the USA, Unimation was interested in selling robots only; it did not produce complete systems based on robots. In the UK, the Unimation subsidiary found that it had to produce systems, which were not always profitable. These were inevitable problems in the first decade of the industrial robot.

But the robot industry, especially that in Japan, and manufacturing industry generally owes a huge debt to Joe Engelberger (the head of Unimation) and the management of Condec for all the pioneering work he and Unimation did on robots. In Japan, Kawasaki Heavy Industries became Unimation's licensee, so that Unimate robots soon dominated the automotive industry, while many of the other robots in use in the 1970s were copies of Unimates. Indeed, it is fair to say that Unimation was responsible for making it possible for the Japanese automotive industry to overtake the US industry in productivity.

But in those early days, the main problem with the robot was its cost. A typical industrial robot would cost £30,000 at a time when average wages were about £3,000 a year in the UK. In the USA, Scandinavia and Germany, the much higher wage rates at that time – up to twice those in the UK – made the robot a more attractive proposition, but even in those countries companies were slow to adopt the new machines. Indeed, many of the early installations outside spot welding were in the factories of robot manufacturers. Thus, they gained experience in use and usually gained in productivity as well.

One reason for the robot being used first in spot welding car bodies was that these factories invariably worked two shifts, and at the time in question – the early 1970s – companies thought they could predict future sales demand accurately. They were all expecting steady growth. Since the robot could spot weld at almost the same rate as a man, it was generally found that one robot replaced about 0.9 men/shift, or about 1.75 men in total. In handling operations in car factories, the robot usually replaces two men. In some other applications, the robot is far less productive. For example, at a battery of injection moulding machines or machine tools, one robot often replaced only 0.3–0.5 men/shift, because it is normal for one man to look after several machines.

If one robot replaces two men earning £3,000 a year, and it costs £30,000, then the payback period – the capital cost divided by the saved labour cost is five years. In most industries, a payback period of two-three years is sought – although this is actually a very shortsighted view where robots are concerned – so most cost accountants would rule out the robot as being uneconomical if the payback period were of the order of five years. But when average wages had moved up to £5,000 a year, things started to look better, especially as robot prices had hardly changed. Now, the payback period was down to three years – in theory. But by this time, about 1980, management realised that wages would continue to increase annually at, say, 10%. Thus, what appeared to be a three-year payback period would in fact turn out to be less. Of course, the robot consumes energy in the form of electricity, and it requires some maintenance, which increase its cost above this example – this subject is discussed more fully later. But then, the worker also requires some fringe benefits, while there are the additional costs of employing him, in pension and sickness benefit insurance.

Indeed, robot manufacturers which use their own robots are apt to say: 'our robots always start on time, they don't get tired or need lunch or tea breaks, and they are never sick. They don't even need any light.' Certainly, if a factory were to be built for completely unmanned operation, it could be very simple, with neither heating nor cooling, and a structure adequate only to keep the interior dry and clean, and to support any cranes.

But such comments about robots are often counterproductive, in that they produce resistance in the workforce. The fact that the robot can repeatedly follow a path precisely, yet a man tends to waver a little towards the end of the day means improved quality. It also means that the man no longer needs to do an arduous job. But men are needed to maintain and programme robots, and to organise the plant – and to feed the robots with parts.

In assessing any potential robot application, it is obviously essential to choose the best type for the job. But it is also necessary to allow for all the robot's advantages and disadvantages in use. First, different working practices will be needed; secondly, the robot will not give the optimum performance from the first job – it will need to be developed to give optimum results. Then, the robot will improve quality where it is replacing manual operation, so long as proper control is maintained. This improved quality can be quantified in reduced inspection and rectification.

For example, a man may just miss one seam when arc welding; the robot will not. If there are variations in the robot's performance, these are likely to follow a pattern that can be analysed, so that compensation can be made. Thus, the robot offers many hidden benefits over manual operation. Not the least of the robot's benefits are its long life. Although it may have a three-year payback period in accountancy terms, its real life is likely to be six to eight years, so its real capital cost is low – especially since it can be reprogrammed to cater for any change in design of the product.

CHAPTER THREE
Developments in controls

UNTIL the microprocessor came along, the robot was ahead of its time – the manipulator was too good for its control system. The controllers were generally limited in capability and were too expensive. Once microprocessors and memory elements were being mass-produced, the whole situation changed. The number of steps and programs that could be used increased, while cost came down. But by 1980, there was need for more memory, and special robot languages to further improve performance. Such developments are now well under way, so that big improvements can be expected in the near future.

In the early days, some 'robots' were not really robots at all; they were manipulators with a certain amount of flexibility. These devices were actuated by electric induction motors, which could be switched on or off only. Thus, the arm would be moved along until a lever tripped a limit switch to switch off the motor. To change a movement of the robot – its program – the operator had to alter the positions of the limit switches. Of course, the action was jerky and unsatisfactory for anything except the simplest motion. Then came sequence controllers. In these, there was a matrix of diodes, and to change a program it was necessary to change the postitions of contact pins.

At that time, hydraulic and pneumatic systems, for which complex but refined valves had been developed, were at a considerable advantage. Although the control valves were expensive, they could control the machine reasonably well. Of course, the precision and performance of the valves deteriorated with wear, so the components had to be made with great precision. In addition, it took some time to change the process steps.

Once microprocessors became generally available in the mid-1970s, program steps could be stored in software, which meant that programs could be changed quickly. Of course, microprocessor control could be used equally well with electrically and hydraulically actuated robots. The essentials in the system are the microprocessor control and encoders which indicate the positions of the various joints and arms. The use of dc servo motors in electrically actuated robots gave a further jump in flexibility, since torque and speed could be varied. Of course, with electro-hydraulic systems, hydraulically-actuated robots can be as flexible as all-electric machines. But the real key was the microprocessor, initially an 8-bit device, such as the Intel 8080. It can process signals very quickly, and can control the robot with great flexibility.

Some of the early machines were controlled by mini-computers, which of course were very expensive, but which had big memories. To reduce cost, microprocessors with 'wire memories' were introduced. These are similar in concept to the core memory of a minicomputer. The steps in the memory can be changed at will, and are not lost if there is a power failure. But since this type of memory is fairly large and costly, the number of steps were limited to 500–600. This is enough for about four programs only. (Fig. 3.1)

Recently, either random access memory (ram) or magnetic bubble memories have been incorporated in robots. An 8-bit microprocessor can access only 64 k bytes of memory, and since quite a lot of this is required for the program instructions, about 16 k bytes were generally available for the user's instructions. In practice, this would give enough memory for the robot to be taught 1,000 points and 600 instructions of where to move, when to start welding, or gripping, and so on. The other part of the memory is needed to hold the operations needed to control the basic operation of the robot – for example, to interpolate a curve from three programmed points, and to convert the desired straight line motion into movements for each of the axes.

One problem with ram is that should the power fail, the memory is lost. Therefore, it is normal to equip the controller with a back-up battery, and to store back-up programs on some other media, such as a floppy disc or tape. To overcome this problem, some companies, notably Fanuc and Hitachi, have adopted the more expensive magnetic bubble memories, which

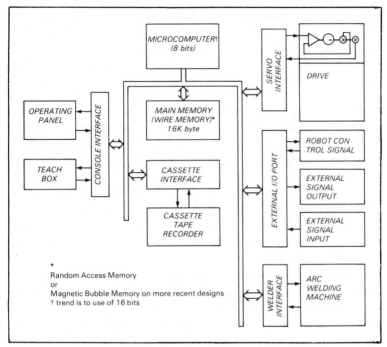

Fig 3.1   Block diagram of total control system

can be removed from the robot controller without loss of memory. These are housed in cassettes, and are ideal for the factory environment. The magnetic bubble memories can hold 1,000 to almost 3,000 steps.

Recently, there has been a trend to the use of 16-bit micro-processors, since these can address a much bigger memory – in theory at least one megabyte – have more powerful instruction sets, can process more complex operations quickly, and can control the positional accuracy of the robot more precisely. For example, with an 8-bit microprocessor, the pulses that determine the minimum distance between successive points have a length of at least 10 microns. With a 16-bit microprocessor, the minimum pulse length is one micron or less. This does not mean that the robot gripper can be placed with an accuracy of one micron, not least because of mechanical deflections in the system, but it does indicate the order of magnitude of the preci-sion. In fact, Fujitsu claims to have developed an experimental robot with a positional accuracy of four microns, allowance for mechanical deflections being incorporated in the control system.

One reason that 16-bit microprocessors are being used on more robots is to improve the speed of programming. Programming can be performed by the use of ordinates, as on an NC machine tool – in fact, robot controllers and NC devices are different versions of the same basic components – but it is more common to use a 'teachbox'. The operator presses a number of buttons in sequence to move the robot through its process, and thus the program is produced. He then reruns it, and can edit the program by making small changes. With painting robots, though, it is normal for the operator to actually take the robot gripper and spray gun through the process, as if he himself were spraying – lead-through teaching. (Fig. 3.2) This system has also been adopted by Trallfa for its arc welding robots.

Normally, the early control systems were such that it was necessary to move the robot through one axis at a time during the teach mode, but with the more modern ones, the robot can be moved through more than one axis at a time. For example, on the Shin Meiwa Robel, each axis is controlled by a lever, which is just pushed away from the operator, and he can push two levers at the same time. But the new ASEA controller goes further; there is one joystick with which the operator can move the robot in any direction. ASEA claims that this device is 25% quicker than normal teachboxes, which seems likely. This

Fig 3.2   Robot control units need to be made smaller

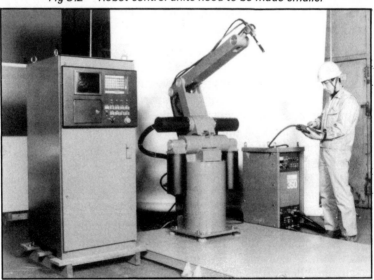

ASEA controller is a 16-bit system, with 100 k byte memory, the main control programs being stored in erasable programmable read only memory (eprom). Additional memory is available, while the system is designed to control a total of nine axes – six in the robot and three external ones, such as those of a workpiece positioner.

The speed of programming depends also on the type of control system in use. Originally, robots were controlled on a 'point-to-point' (PTP) method, but now 'continuous path' (CP) control has come into use. With PTP, the operator must move the robot not just to each corner or beginning of curve of the proposed path, but he must also identify points on a straight line – usually at intervals of about 15mm. Several PTP control systems have special routines to speed up programming. For example, to make the robot follow a semicircle it is normally necessary to put the controller in the circular mode, and identify three points. Where the angle of the gripper is important, as in arc welding, the operator needs to move the gripper to the correct angle at each point. In doing so, of course, he may move the actual tip of the tool from the correct position.

With the KUKA CP control system, the tool angle needs to be set only at the beginning of the program, and then it is automatically adjusted to retain correct inclination. Then, to trace a straight line, the operator merely indicates the points at the beginning and end of the line. This greatly speeds up teaching of all jobs, but there is also a special routine for palletising. The operator indicates only the corner points of the pallet; the number of points or positions in x, y and z axes; the loading and unloading direction from the side and from above; and the number of rows.

The CP control system can also be used to synchronise the actions of the robot with a moving conveyor. Of course, these conveyors do not move at a constant speed, and sometimes stop. To programme the robot, the part is moved along the conveyor, and is stopped at the operating point. Then, the robot is programmed with the part stationary.

The Kawasaki Unimate 6060 controller has a combination of PTP and CP control systems. PTP is used for most operations, but where greater accuracy is needed, such as when the robot has to weld around a corner with a small radius, the CP system is used.

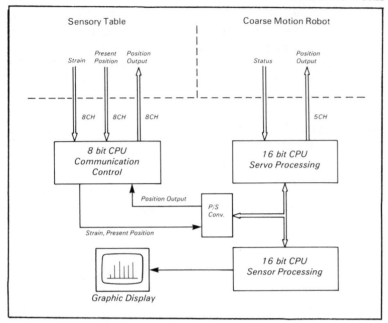

Fig 3.3 Multi-process controllers point the way ahead

Although these controllers are a considerable advance, special computer languages are needed for robots. These should be 'high-level' languages, which means that with very simple instructions, the robot can be programmed to be taught very complex tasks. CP is a higher level language than PTP, but in arc welding, it is desirable to be able to press one control, and then identify the dimensions to programme a square or circular weld path. In assembly, it should be sufficient to type 'insert' for the robot to insert a part in the assembly. (Fig. 3.3)

Various high level languages have been developed. There is the VAL language developed for the Unimation Puma, while Stanford University in the USA developed its AL language, which has been modified by other researchers, including those at Institut fur Informatik III, Karlsruhe, Germany, and Tokyo University, Japan. Such languages as these need to be turned into commercial packages before the robot teach/control system reaches the state where it can be used easily and safely for any job, from manipulating a contouring tool over a known shape, to arc welding or assembly.

In addition, as visual, tactile sensors, and other devices to help the robot learn functions come into use, so multiple processors and much larger memories will become commonplace. For robots with these sensors to be exploited fully, these high level languages will be essential.

CHAPTER FOUR
How cost-effective are robots?

IN manufacture, profits are determined by overall production costs, and like any other piece of automation, a robot must pay. However, when one or two robots are installed, it is absurd to spend a lot of time justifying their cost, or rejecting the purchase because the robots seem expensive. Such installations should be considered experimental. When the robots have been working in a number of jobs, and factors such as their rate of working, the ancillary equipment needed, downtime and effect on manning levels have been established, attempts at costing a major installation can be made. Where it is not practicable to obtain such data with an experimental set-up, then guideline data should be used.

The actual cost of a robot installation, be it a few robots for handling, a dozen for arc welding, spot welding, or assembly, will depend on the ancillary equipment as much as on the robots. Particularly for assembly, many extra devices are needed to check that parts are available, and that they have been installed. For many installations, direct computer control is advisable. On the other hand, for arc welding a simple turntable and fixtures will suffice, and for handling virtually no ancillary equipment is necessary.

Whatever the application, a robot is a relatively costly piece of equipment, so it must be fully utilised in order to recoup the capital costs. Therefore, when robots are to be installed in any department or section, efforts should be made to ensure that they can operate for the maximum period each day. Ideally, 24 hour operation should be planned, and two shifts should be adopted if that is impractical. In this case, it is not a question of trebling production capacity, by going from one to three shifts. Instead, fewer machines should be installed so that the output on three shifts is little more than that obtained previously on one shift. The higher operating efficiency should result in increased sales, and the level of equipment should reflect this fact. Where practical, the robots should operate unmanned, or with the minimum of manning at night. Where it is impractical to operate for more than one shift, the robot should be operated unmanned during lunch breaks and for some overtime to amortize the costs reasonably quickly. On current cost levels, though, robots are unlikely to be cost-effective if they are never used for more than eight hours a day.

Generally, of course, the cost of a robot is equated with that of labour, mainly because in the early days, robots were used to do jobs that were normally done manually – handling or spot welding operations requiring considerable dexterity. But costs should also be compared with those of hard automation. In either case, allowance needs to be made for the different capabilities of the robot and man or conventional machine. These vary according to the application, but experience shows that the performance of a robot in different jobs and on different shift arrangements is:

	Number of men replaced by one robot		
	One shift	*Two shifts*	*Three shifts*
Assembly and handling	0.3–1.0	0.6–2	1.0–3.0
Spot welding	0.7–0.9	1.5–1.75	2.1–2.5
Arc welding	0.5–0.75	1.0–1.5	1.5–2.2

With wage rates of about £3/h net, the cost of employing a worker in Britain is £4–5/h, or around £9,000 a year. Thus, if the robot costs £30,000, and the ancillary equipment per robot costs £10,000, then the repayment time for the £40,000 is:

$$\frac{£40,000}{£9,000 \times n}$$

, where n is the number of workers replaced by each robot – usually 1 to 1.75. Thus, the repayment or 'payback' period is 2.3–4.4 years – too long for most company accountants.

In reality, of course, the cost equation is more complex. There is the cost of maintenance, power and overhauls, hidden costs that are equivalent to the extra cost of employing a worker. Against that, the robot has a useful life of about eight years. On this basis, Unimation Inc calculated the life cost of a Unimate robot on the following basis in 1981: (Fig. 4.1)

Hourly cost of Robot	
Price of Unimate	$50,000
Cost of installation	$12,000
Interest rate	15%
Hourly cost on two shift operation in 1981:	
Depreciation	$1.56/h
Interest payment	$1.10/h
Installation	$0.80/h
Power	$0.40/h
Overhauls (two)	$0.40/h
Maintenance	$1.15/h
Total cost	$5.41/h

At that time, the gross hourly wage rate in the US automotive industry was around $19/h, so on this basis, the robot seems very cheap. General Motors plans to install 14,000 robots by 1990, and if each robot saves $13/h, it is calculated that the company will make a gross saving of $728 million a year, a phenomenal but theoretical sum.

In reality, though, the automotive workers were paid much more highly than those in US industry generally, or in the motor industries elsewhere, while companies were not prepared to accept Unimation's claim that the robot should be depreciated over eight years. So, if all the costs have to be recouped over a three year span, then the cost is very different. The cost of depreciation and interest increase to $7/h, so that overall costs come to about $10/h. Since at that time, a wage rate of $11/h was more realistic in the USA and many other industrialized nations the advantage of the robot was only marginal – but it is increasing continually.

More realistically, the robot would be depreciated over five years, since the evidence is that robot life is at least this much. On five-year depreciation, the cost is about $8 or £4/h. Thus, if one robot replaces one man, the robot will be cheaper, even on British labour rates. With two shift operation, the robot is usually significantly cheaper than manual labour, because it replaces more than one man. Of course, the real cost equation will vary according to the ancillary equipment needed.

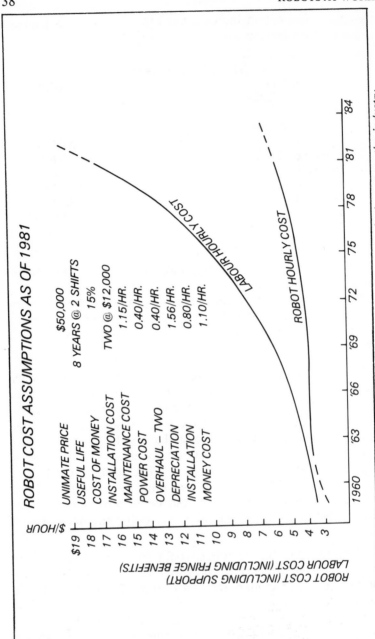

ROBOT COST ASSUMPTIONS AS OF 1981

UNIMATE PRICE	$50,000
USEFUL LIFE	8 YEARS @ 2 SHIFTS
COST OF MONEY	15%
INSTALLATION COST	TWO @ $12,000
MAINTENANCE COST	1.15/HR.
POWER COST	0.40/HR.
OVERHAUL – TWO	0.40/HR.
DEPRECIATION	1.56/HR.
INSTALLATION	0.80/HR.
MONEY COST	1.10/HR.

LABOUR HOURLY COST

ROBOT HOURLY COST

$/HOUR

$19 18 17 16 15 14 13 12 11 10 9 8 7 6 5 4 3

ROBOT COST (INCLUDING SUPPORT)
LABOUR COST (INCLUDING FRINGE BENEFITS)

1960 '63 '66 '69 '72 '75 '78 '81 '84

Fig 4.1   History of labour cost and the history of Unimate robot costs in the automotive industry

In assembly, hard automation is generally considered acceptable if the cost is about £3,000 per station, and so this has become the cost target for small assembly robots – but one that seems impossible at the time of writing. In Japan, the Scara robots made by such companies as Sankyo Seiki, Yamaha and Nitto Seiki cost about £10,000, but are coming into use despite this cost penalty. The reason is that they are being used principally in the automotive parts and consumer electronics industries, where new models are introduced to replace existing ones at alarming speed. In the 1970s, the life of a product was about four years, but by the early 1980s, companies were finding that products, and therefore the hard automation used to produce them, were being redesigned after only two years. By contrast, a robot line could remain virtually unchanged for at least five years.

In these factories, cycle times are usually very short – 3–20s – so one robot normally replaces only one station of an automated line. In theory, therefore, the robot is at a disadvantage of about 30% in hourly costs – say, 52p/h, against 39p/h. But this was offset by the reduced design costs – it was no longer necessary to redesign the line every two years. Then, in many robot lines, it became possible to operate for three shifts a day, with little or no manning on the night shift. Of course, many robots were installed where manual labour had been used before, and in those cases, the ability to operate three shifts a day, with one shift unmanned was critical in making the installation cost effective.

But in any application, be it to replace hard automation or manual operation, the robot has hidden benefits, which can have a substantial effect on the real costs. For example, in spot welding, the robot can weld with great precision throughout the shift, whereas the manual operator occasionally misses welds, and places them at irregular intervals. Once robots are adopted, the number of welds can be reduced, yet the stiffness of the structure can be improved. In addition, the actual consistency of the welding almost invariably improves the quality of the product in a number of ways. This can be seen in lower warranty claims and less lost time in assembly operations further down the line, but these results are likely to underestimate the benefits, not least because better quality increases repeat orders. In arc welding, or arduous handling jobs, the poor working conditions will lead the operators to take frequent breaks, and in some cases, it is necessary to provide a relief operator. With robots, these breaks disappear, so output increases, even though this too is difficult to quantify.

In complex lines, the fact that each robot is a separate unit, which can be reprogrammed not just for a different product, but also to take over temporarily from another robot results in increased plant utilisation. For example, if one machine in a transfer line stops, the whole line stops. Of course, to counterbalance this problem, it is normal to divide a complex line into sections. But because a spare robot or standby operator can make the welds or do the assembly instead of a temporarily inoperative robot, 'downtime' in robot lines is much lower than in conventional hard automation lines. In addition, where automated lines are divided into sections, it is normal to have buffer stores between each section to allow for these breakdowns. With robots, much smaller buffer stores can be used, thus reducing the cost of work-in-progress.

For example, the downtime in an automated line might be 25%, yet with the same number of failures, the figure for the robot line is likely to be less than 15%. With spot welding, arc welding or spraying, where other robots can be instantly be reprogrammed, total downtime can be kept to a few per cent only. In fact, in many installations, the downtime of a robot section of a line is claimed to be only 2–3%, and in other cases, a total downtime of 10% with robots is achieved where 35% was being achieved with hard automation.

Of course, when cost engineers are faced with the company's first robot installation, they are likely to anticipate a higher proportion of downtime than with their existing machinery, and not a lower one. Because robots can be reprogrammed in the event of a failure back down the line, this is a fundamental error; it is essential to recognise that a failure in a robot should not affect the whole line. At worst, the line might be stopped for a few seconds while the computer reprograms the robots further down the line. To give complete flexibility of course, each robot needs to have some spare time in the cycle, or there needs to be a spare robot station. But with some thought, it is possible to arrange for the robots to operate in such a way that the line only stops when there is a shortage of workpieces, or a complete jam. Thus, in determining the number of robots needed, a lower downtime should be allowed for than with hard automation. If the downtime is 30% for hard automation, and 10% for a robot line, then the installed capacity of an automated line needs to be 1,300 a day, against 1,100 a day for the robot line. In both cases, expected output would be 1,000 a day. Therefore the robot line will be smaller and relatively cheaper than might have been anticipated.

Of course, many problems that can be encountered in complex manufacturing systems are eliminated with the introduction of robots. In one car factory, a massive multiwelder used at a framing station once jammed in the closed position because a welding electrode had welded itself to the panels. It was reported that the factory was shut down for two days as a result of that failure. The elimination of such events would hardly be included in a cost comparison of robots against hard automation, but it is a distinct advantage. Thus, if the cost of a robot line comes anywhere near the cost of hard automation or manual operation, it is likely to pay handsomely – thanks to its fringe benefits.

CHAPTER FIVE
Spot welding – the first major use

SPOT welding was the first major use for robots, and after a slow start it has spread very rapidly. But during the first decade or so, the type of robots used, and the way they were used changed as manufacturers gained experience. That evolution is a pointer to what is likely to happen in other applications. Not only have special-purpose robots been developed, but the amount of flexibility has been increased dramatically. Several companies have reached the stage where models can be changed completely with only minor changes in tooling, while several completely different bodies can go down one line.

Traditionally, a combination of press welders and manual welding had been used in body assembly. The number of press welders depended on the production volume. For example, it was standard practice to use a multi-station press welder to weld the crossmembers and brackets to the underbody, while the side assemblies and doors were also welded on special-purpose machines. Often, small sub-assemblies were welded manually either at pedestal welders, or on carousel fixtures.

At the critical stage where the underbody, sides and roof came together, it was normal to use fixtures on a carousel, with manual welding, or a press welder. However, at the stages following the framing, called 'respot' welding, where the remaining spot welds are added, it was normal to use manual welding. But it was possible to fully automate body welding without robots, as Daimler-Benz showed at its Sindelfingen factory near Stuttgart. It adopted press welders for all stages of manufacture, from sub-assemblies through the respot stages to achieve 99% automated welding. However, that was a very inflexible line designed to handle only one body type at 70 an hour.

The multiwelder lines installed by Daimler-Benz were conceptually similar to those that had been used for the underbodies and side assemblies. But generally, in the 1960s, the respot welding was done manually with the bodies continually moving on conveyors. In some cases, these lines were in fact oval carousels, and in others were straight lines. In either case, the bodies were held in jigs which moved down the track as the welding was done. Of course, owing to manufacturing tolerances, the jigs were not identical in size, but this was not critical. In addition, as the body and jig moved down the line, so it might move a little from side to side of the track; again that was not a problem, since the operator compensated quite naturally.-

But for these reasons it was not an easy matter to install, say two robots, in a conventional line to see how they worked. For example, when British Leyland (BL) bought its first Unimate robot in about 1970, the company installed it experimentally for welding up sub-assemblies. The reason was that traditionally, small sub-assemblies were welded manuallly on a series of stationary fixtures, the assembly being transferred by hoist or carousel between stations. Therefore it was easier to install one robot to see how it operated. Ford of UK adopted a different approach with its first robot; a standard pedestal welder was used, and the Unimate moved the sub-assembly, previously tacked together. The places where welds had to be made were presented in sequence to the welder, whose operation was controlled by the robot. Meanwhile, the robot operated the welder.

Thus, before robots could be used, many changes in concept were needed. First, it was thought that the body needed to be stationary during welding; secondly, each body had to be located accurately so that the robot, which would always weld in the same position, would make contact with the welding flange. Also, since some of the normal cycle time would be lost as the body was moved from station to station – typically 20–30s – the actual time for welding would be less than with manual welding. The technical problems were not great, but the use of robots for respot welding did involve a lot of investment, and in the early days, no one was sure how accurately, how fast, and how reliably the robots would operate. Since these are precisely the worries engineers and managers express about robots in other applications, the experience with body welding is valuable.

In any event, the first major installation of robots for body welding was in 1970, long before Daimler-Benz built that line, when General Motors (GM) installed a robot welding line at its Lordstown factory in the USA. The reasons for the use of robots were not what might be expected now. Up to that time, GM had been making large cars, at a rate of about 60 an hour, and it started to build a smaller car, the Chevrolet Vega. Since the profit margin would be less on the Vega than on full-size cars, GM decided on a production rate of 100 a hour. For most sub-assemblies, press welders were used, but it was decided that at 100 an hour, it would not be practical to do the respot welding manually. So, robots were chosen.

GM built a shuttle conveyor to transfer the bodies between stations, the bodies being locked in a stationary position during welding. The robots were then installed in rows on each side of the line, just as the men had previously worked on each side. Altogether, there were 22 robots in eight stations – 11 on each side of the line. Their main function was to weld around the door apertures and along the sills. Each robot made about 20 welds.

To do that job, considerable dexterity was needed, since the robot needs to be able to make welds around corners with small radii. It also needed to be able to move across to the centre of the body, and to move out of the way at the end of the cycle, which only lasted about 36s, including the time for the shuttle conveyor to move. Thus, machines with five axes of freedom were chosen. This concept was followed by Fiat in Italy, and then by Nissan and Toyota in Japan. In all these lines, Unimates were used, although in Japan, these were mixed with Toshiba Tosman robots that were Unimate lookalikes. (Fig. 5.1)

It is interesting that Fiat also switched to robots for a specific reason. It had encountered considerable industrial unrest at its Mirafiori factory in Turin, and much of the trouble occurred in the respot welding line. This was not altogether surprising, since the work was tiring, and the line was in the middle of a large dark factory that became very hot in summer. So, Fiat decided to install robots, to overcome the industrial problems and increase productivity at the same time. In Japan, too, the early installations of robots at respot lines were aimed at eliminating a tiring job as much as to increase productivity.

But those early installations showed up some disadvantages in the robots for body welding, and also sparked off some ideas for

Fig 5.1 One of two synchronised robot welding lines for the British Leyland Metro at Longbridge, UK

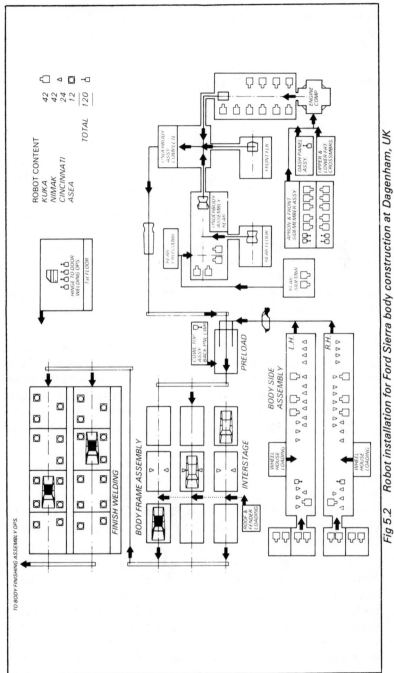

Fig 5.2   Robot installation for Ford Sierra body construction at Dagenham, UK

new approaches. For example, it was generally felt by the engineers involved that the robots were too large and slow, and that they had more degrees of motion than was desirable. Then, the transformers for welding were mounted remotely and, to provide sufficient power to overcome the losses in the cables, large transformers were needed. Because the cables were continually being flexed, they were liable to break. Nevertheless, these early installations proved very satisfactory from a reliability point of view. Initially, extra robots were installed to take over from a robot that had broken down, but this soon proved unnecessary. But these problems meant that the robots were not as cost-effective as they should have been.

To overcome the problem of cable breakage, some robots with transformers built into the arms were developed for spot welding, by companies such as Comau of Italy and KUKA of Germany. Then, Toshiba developed a very simple robot for Nissan. This was a three-axis machine, with a small gun carried on a block that could move vertically and horizontally on a pair of slides. It was used to make spotwelds on flanges that were virtually straight. (Fig. 5.2)

Another major problem was that although the robots could generally position the spot within 1mm of the desired position, the jigs used previously could not present the body to the robot in the correct position. Therefore, much more precise jigging than had been used previously was needed. With manual welding, of course, no such care was needed, since the operator could compensate accordingly.

In addition, the full potential of the robots was not always exploited. For example, in many cases the robots were used to work on only one or two body types, such as two- and four-door, but always on the same basic shell. Clearly, to exploit the robots properly, they should be used to weld up many different bodies in random order.

In addition, at that time it was not practical to use a robot to hold the body for welding. The most critical stage of body welding is where the side assemblies and underbody assembly come together. These must be positioned and held together accurately while they are tack welded together. One solution was to use fixtures with manual welding; another was to use multiwelders; a third was to use special-purpose welding machines which could be used for one or two models.

For example, when it became deeply involved in robot welding, Nissan carried out an extensive programme to see just how few welds were needed to hold the body together, so that the maximum number of welds could be made by robots, with the body unjigged. It found that less than 40 welds were needed. Obviously, the welding machine and fixture that makes only 40 welds is relatively inexpensive, especially if it is built into a structure which remains unchanged when the body design is changed.

New concept – Robogate

Fiat developed its Robogate system in conjunction with Comau, its production engineering subsidiary, to take full advantage of robots. In the Robogate system, the framing and respot welding are carried out in special four-post fixtures by robots. The main sub-assemblies are loosely assembled on special fixtures at a previous station, and are held in position by tags between the various main sub-assemblies. Then, the body is transferred by Robotrailer to the first Robogate. The Robotrailer follows cables buried in the floor.

Each Robogate is essentially a fixture to locate the jig carrying the body, and clamps that hold the body sub-assemblies in the correct position for welding. There are two, three or four robots at each Robogate, some being mounted on the floor, and some on the gantries of the four-post structure. (Fig. 5.3, 5.4)

When the body enters the Robogate, its fixture is lowered on to four locating points, and then it is welded up by the robots. After welding, the body and Robotrailer move on to the next Robogate, these being arranged in parallel. Up to six Robogates are used to make the 500 or so welds needed for framing and respot welding. They can handle up to about 60 bodies an hour.

This system gives great flexibility, since bodies can enter the Robogate from both ends. For example, a large body can enter from one end, and be picked up in its clamps, and there can be three or four versions of that model going through the same Robogate line. Then, another model can enter, alternately, or in random sequence, from the other end, to be picked up by its set of clamps. Of course, the body type and model type can be processed in random order according to demand. In addition, it is possible for one Robogate to do the work of another one in

Fig 5.3   Fiat developed its Robogate system with Comau

Fig 5.4   Robogate is essentially a fixture to locate the body

the event of a failure. On the other hand, the Robogate system does take up a lot of space. But when the body design is changed completely, only the jigging inside the structures has to be renewed.

In Japan, other methods have been used to gain flexibility. For example, Honda devised its own type of fixture for much of its welding, but uses some Unimate robots and some simple robots of its own design. At its Suzuka factory, Honda uses four Unimate 4000 robots to make welds on the underbody assembly, but 75 of its own robots to weld up sub-assemblies. These units can have three–, four– or five axes of freedom, and consist of a horizontal slide so that the robot can move into and away from the body; a scissor mechanism to provide vertical travel; and jaws that can articulate on vertical and horizontal axes. An extra degree of freedom can be built into the wrist. These are very compact and simple units, and they are usually arranged in groups of three or four at one station. For example, three are used to weld up the rear side assembly, making 40 welds in a cycle of 41s. (Fig. 5.5)

A somewhat similar device has been developed by British Federal Welder in the UK for use in 'custom-built' welding lines, one of the first applications being the underbody line for the BL

Fig 5.5   At Honda three robots weld up a rear side member

LM10 car. In the first station, welds are made by a small multi-welder, and then there are three robot stations – with four, two and two robots respectively. In this case, welding guns with long reach were needed – in fact, the jaws are 700mm long, and they needed to be able to move in three axes. Therefore, British Federal Welder chose a design based on Cartesian co-ordinate motion in which the robot arm and welding gun are integrated. This line is designed to produce 50 bodies an hour.

After it had installed a number of robots in respot lines in its factories in Japan, Nissan decided it needed a smaller version of the Unimate 2000 robot for body welding, and so laid out a basic design which it then gave to Kawasaki Heavy Industries, Unimation Inc's Japanese licensee. This was basically a smaller version of the Unimate 2000, mounted upside down on a rail along which it could slide. Kawasaki turned this idea, dubbed BBS, or building block system by Nissan, into a fully-fledged design – the Unimate 6060. The 6060 consists of a head, free to slide along a rail, a pillar hanging down from the head, and a horizontal arm. The pillar can pivot through some 70° on an axis parallel with the slide, while the arm can pivot on the pillar, and the wrist has two degrees of freedom. Actuation is hydraulic, with one hydraulic system actuating up to three

Fig 5.6   Kawasaki Unimate 6060 robots installed at Toyota

robots, while one controller is adequate for six robots. The 6060 can make welds at the rate of one every two seconds.

In Nissan's first installation, six 6060 arms are used at one station to weld side assemblies for Nissan Cherry cars, four different versions going down the line. The cycle time is 45s, and each robot makes eight welds in about 20s, the remaining time being needed to move the body side between stations. The 6060 arm has both continuous path and point-to-point control systems, the continuous path system being used only at critical areas, such as tight corners, and the point-to-point system otherwise. (Fig.5.6)

But the most unusual feature of the installation is that the six robots are mounted in two rows, three robots sliding along the same rail. The rails are mounted on a four-post structure above the line, and the control systems are carried conveniently above the structure. Thus, the installation becomes a standard welding unit, just as the Robogate does.

To some extent, the system developed by Mitsubishi Motors is similar to the 6060 in that the robots generally hang down from massive four-post structures, and they are also small. Mitsubishi Heavy industries developed a range of modular robots specially for body welding. The Mitsubishi Robitus is a Cartesian coordinate robot, which can be mounted on a base on the floor – with or without slide – or can be mounted on an overhead gantry or on a pillar. Thus, the robots can easily be integrated with welding lines, and each robot can be assembled with the precise number of axes of freedom necessary – usually four or five. (Fig. 5.7) (Fig. 5.8)

At Mitsubishi Motors' Okazaki factory, about 100 robots are installed in one line where four models are produced – coupe and saloon models sharing a common front-wheel drive underbody, and rear-drive coupe and saloon models with similar underbodies but different wheelbases. All four cars have completely different external panels. The volume of each model would not be high enough to warrant the use of four different lines – each is produced at the rate of about 200 a day on two shifts. Even on two lines, the production rate, of 400 a day would not have been economic, especially since the model mix once production was under way was not as the marketing people had predicted; in other words, the robots have allowed Mit-

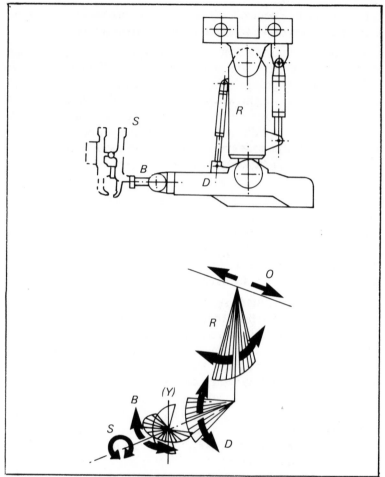

*Fig 5.7   The BBS robot showing (top) the side view and (bottom)
movement of the axes*

subishi to produce four models economically, and without the robots, they would not have been able to do so. (Fig. 5.9)

In Europe, Ford has also adopted robots suspended from gantries to weld up the Escort. There are 12 of these Nimak robots, which each have two arms suspended from gantries, and 11 floor-mounted KUKA robots in the underbody line. Significantly, both these robots have transformers just behind the gun to eliminate the need for cables. The Nimak robots are used mainly to weld up the engine bay, which is a very complicated structure requiring considerable dexterity. Ford decided

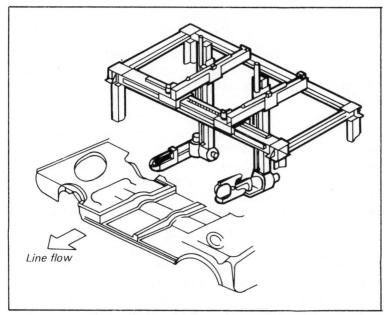

Fig 5.8   Mitsubishi robots for welding underbodies

Fig 5.9   A Mitsubishi robot welding a rear skirt

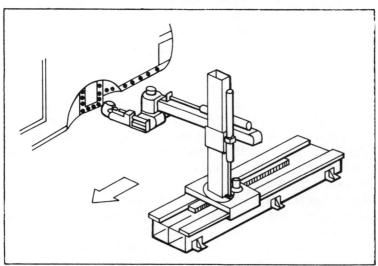

that it was best to use robots where the welding was complex, and to retain press welders for the simpler weld paths. (Fig. 5.9)

Toyo Kogyo and Toyota have retained conventional-looking lines for their more recent robot installations, but have adopted simpler robots. For example, Toyo Kogyo uses 14 robots a line to weld up the underbodies of its 323 model, using presswelders only for sub-assemblies. Where a long reach is needed, Unimate 4000 robots are used, but otherwise Unimate 3040s, which have four axes of movement are adopted. The 3000 series robots consist of a telescopic arm on a telescopic column. The robot can also traverse on a slide parallel with the line, while the wrist can articulate in one axis as well. These robots, in conjunction with some Unimate 2000s are also used for respot welding.

Toyota's Tahara plant is a good example of the flexibility gained with robot welding. There, Toyota produces the Celica Liftback and Celica Supra, which have different length wheelbases, and the Soarer. In fact, the body of the Supra and Liftback models are identical from the windscreen rearwards. Then, the front end of the underbody of the Supra and Soarer are the same, but in other respects these two models are completely different. So, there are three different body styles, and to suit different power units and suspensions, there are a total of seven different underbodies. Yet all go down the same line at a cycle of just under two min.

To cope with this variey, Toyota is using 90 robots, including 22 in the underbody line. These are all Unimates – 4000s, 2000s and 6060s, and together with some small press welders, they make 90% of the welds, leaving 10% to be made manually. On the underbody line, there are eight Unimate 4000s and 14 small 6060 arms.

Whereas Nissan mounts the 6060 arms on overhead gantries, Toyota has mounted most of the 6060 arms on short pillars so they can move quickly into the body. The arm is mounted on its side on the pillar, so that it pivots on vertical axes. Thus, the articulation of the arm is used to move the welding gun into and away from the body quickly. Each robot is preprogrammed, and as each underbody starts on the line, so the production control computer inputs the necessary data so that the correct program is used at the right time for the right underbody. The side assemblies are also welded mainly by robots, with the different versions going down the same line. (Fig. 5.10)

Fig 5.10   Side assemblies can be welded easily by robots with little tooling

Toyota uses a mixture of multiwelders and robots to weld the sides and roof to the floor at the critical 'framing' stage. To cope with the different bodies, the multiwelders have multiple clamps and welding guns, the clamps being moved into position by pneumatic rams as needed. The final 'respot' or finish welding is carried out by a mixture of Unimate 2000 and 6060 arms.

In all these applications the body is stationary during welding, but in the USA GM has installed some Cincinnati robots to weld bodies moving continuously on a conveyor. In some respects,

Fig 5.11   Typical arrangement of Unimate robots spot welding Cargo
cabs at the Ford plant, Langley, UK

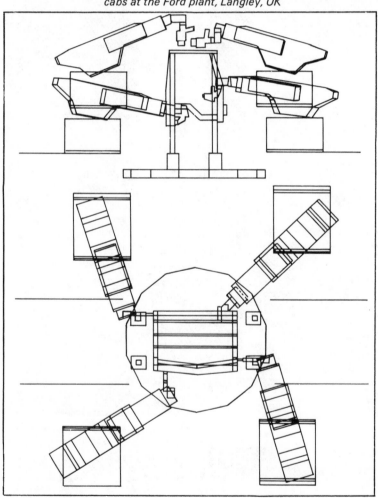

this results in a simpler line, in that a shuttle and fixtures are not needed. However, the bodies must still be positioned accurately at the welding stations. On the other hand, different bodies can be handled easily on one line.

Although robots are generally used for large volume production, involving a cycle of 40–60s, they are equally applicable for lower rates of production. The difference is, of course, that the cycle time is longer, and that each robot makes more welds. Unimates are used by Lancia in Italy for relatively low volume. Then, Ford has installed four Unimate 4000 robots to carry out respot welding – 270 welds are made – on truck cabs at its Langley plant in the UK on a cycle of 3min 20s. In the Ford application, the cab is delivered from the framing area by conveyor to a turntable on which it is clamped and welded. Since Ford's truck manufacturing engineers had no previous experience with robots, they decided that the clamping should be identical to that used for framing. (Fig. 5.11)

The robots are equally spaced, and they all weld simultaneously. They go through one welding sequence, then the table is turned through 90°, and they complete the welding. Afterwards, the table rotates through 180° so that the cab can be transported automatically to the next station. Should one robot break down, the table can be rotated through 270° to allow the robot opposite the one that has broken down to make the necessary welds. On a practical note, several safeguards were needed to prevent damage in the event of a problem such as an electrode that had stuck to the panel. For example, limit switches were added to indicate that the points were open, and that the robot could proceed to the next command. Of course, a man does not need to be told that the electrodes have stuck, but a robot does. (Fig. 5.12)

KUKA has devised various systems aimed at flexibility and lower volumes, such as those of BMW, the German car company. For example, there is a turnover fixture, like a spit, to carry the body at a station where 80 welds are made by two robots in about 3 min. The bodies are loaded and unloaded from the upper side of the fixture, while the robots are welding below.

In another development aimed at body welding, KUKA has produced a robot that incorporates one electrode only. The robot is carried on a gantry overhead, and can traverse across

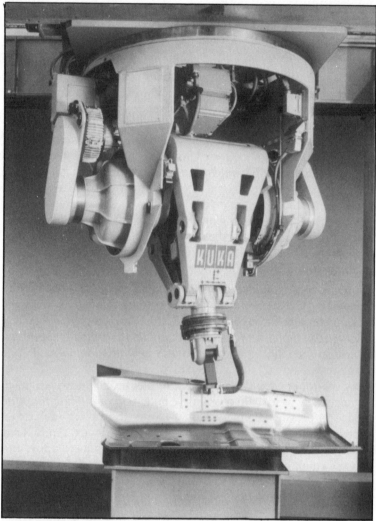

Fig 5.12   KUKA's five-axis all-electric portal welding robot

the sub-assembly or body. The arm has basically two degrees of freedom, while the electrode can be tilted so that it is at right-angles to the surface of the panel. There are backing electrodes beneath the panel, while the transformer is mounted on one of the pillars of the structure carrying the robot, which is called the IR 200. This design gives the flexibility of the robot at low cost. Of course, it can only be used where the movements are fairly simple, but is ideal for sub-assembly welding. (Fig. 5.13)

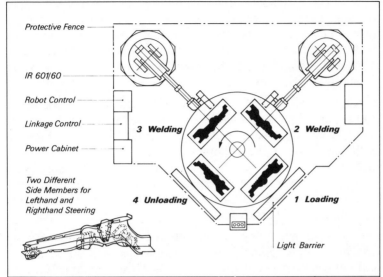

Fig 5.13   Two portal robots welding sub-assemblies

In one application, the IR 200 robot is used to weld wheelarches together. There is a turntable with four stations, each equipped with different backing electrodes. The wheelarches are clamped to the backing electrode fixtures, and are moved into position for welding by alternate clockwise and anti-clockwise rotation of the turntable through 90 deg. Some 56 spots are made in 140s, some through two thicknesses, and others through three thicknesses. These robots are also used to weld floorpans, a line of 12 being used in conjunction with floor-mounted robots.

These examples show that the spot-welding robot is gradually evolving from the universal machine with five or six axes of freedom to a special-purpose device, designed principally for high volume manufacture. Clearly, as time goes on, spot welding robots will become more specialised, and will usually be based on a modular design concept. As a result, their use will become almost universal for spot welding assemblies needed in large volumes – not just for cars, but also for domestic appliances and other products with steel housings.

For small companies, though, the universal robot without too many axes of freedom has many advantages. It can be used equally well to move sub-assemblies through a pedestal welder, to weld sub-assemblies at simple fixtures, or to carry out respot welding. Indeed, there is no reason why two robots could not carry out a complete respot welding programme involving 300–500 spots in a cycle time of about 10 minutes. In that case, the robots would preferably work on two shifts, to produce about 100 assemblies a day.

Alternatively, with four robots, the respot welding for about 300 assemblies a day could be done on two shifts. Then, simpler robots could be used to weld up the critical sub-assemblies. In both cases, once the robots were installed, they would last through several model changes, and so their real cost, with amortisation over the real lifespan, and not according to accountants' preconceived notions which are based on conventional equipment, would be low.

Of course, according to conventional wisdom, robots are too costly for such applications – but only because the managers and engineers involved think in terms of high-volume lines. In fact, four universal robots cost about £100,000, while the fixtures need not be expensive as only one or two stations would be needed. Since the welding could be done in a very small area, overheads would be low, and of course, as is always the case with robot installations, labour costs would be reduced, while quality would improve.

Thus, automated welding can be provided at relatively low cost for low volumes, so long as the managers concerned use their imagination, and do not slavishly follow what is being done elsewhere. But in any application, the layout should be such that several different models can be processed on one line, and that full model changes make the minimum of equipment obsolete; in that way companies will be able to respond to the challenges of the future.

CHAPTER SIX
Handling

INITIALLY, the robot seemed ideal for handling. After all, it can move in the same way as the human arm, and it is designed to carry loads. In practice, most handling operations proved to be bad applications for robots, which were too expensive, too slow, and which required too much ancillary equipment. Gradually, however, some good applications were found, and now robots are used extensively in two main areas – where the workpieces are heavy or hot, and where the robot gives a significant decrease in manning, as in loading and unloading at NC machine tools. The number of applications is increasing, though, as more inexpensive special-purpose handling robots are being developed.

If a robot is used to unload a machine, it is preferable for the robot to place the workpieces directly into a pallet. If a man is used, not only can he do this, but while the machine is operating, he can walk over to another machine, and unload that. In addition, when a pallet is full, he can start loading another one, and tell the materials handler to take the pallet away – or place the pallet on a conveyor.

But the robot is limited in what it can do. It can unload the workpieces, and it can be programmed to place the workpieces in sequence in the different slots in the pallet, so long as sufficient memory is available. But generally, the robot is stuck at one machine, so it is likely to spend most of its time idle – perhaps working for 15 s every minute. To be cost-effective, it needs to be able to load and unload from several machines, but that means it needs to operate much more quickly. Also, to pick up parts coming along a belt conveyor, vision sensing, to indicate the position and orientation of the part is needed. But in a real world, the use of vision sensing for this job is probably not the answer; with simpler devices, it should be possible to orientate the parts.

In any event, robots are used for certain specialised handling applications, such as in forges and diecasting foundries, at NC machine tools, and as subsidiary handling devices for assembly robots – the handling robot is not interchangeable with an assembly robot, owing to different levels of accuracy. If it is interchangeable, it has been overdesigned.

Experimental

When it developed a range of robots, Volkswagen used several experimentally in various handling applications which demonstrate the possibilities. For example, one was used to remove cast iron crankshafts that had just been cast from a conveyor. The robot was programmed to fill pallets alternately – first the one on the left of the line, and then on the right. This was a prototype robot, so it was not particularly precise. Therefore, no efforts were made to place the crankshafts with precision; they were simply dropped into the pallets. Because the crankshafts weighed around 15kg, and they were hot, two men were normally needed to load the pallets. In this case, therefore, the robot replaced two men working on each shift – a total of four men. When the robot was installed, wage rates at Volkswagen were about £6,000 a year, and the robot would have cost £30,000 if purchased from a robot manufacturer. Therefore, the nominal payback period was only 15 months. (Fig. 6.1)

In another application, a robot was used to transfer a sub-assembly of a 1.5m long steel tube and brackets through a two-station automatic welder. Since the welds were straight, requiring little dexterity, this approach was thought preferable to robot welding. The robot, working to a 15s cycle, picks up the assembly from a conveyor, places it in the first welding machine, then transfers it to the second machine, finally placing it on a conveyor. Then another robot transfers the finished assemblies to a pallet. Previously, two men were needed on each shift at the welding machines, and a third for palletizing, so the two robots replaced a total of six men, to give a cost-effective solution. In this case, a U-shape gripper with very wide jaws was needed, but that was the only ancillary equipment, except for the fences to enclose the robot and machines.

*Fig 6.1   Volkswagen robot being used to handle fabrications at
automatic welding machines*

Volkswagen also produced a simpler robot which was used to handle panels between machines in the press shop, and installed four in one line. This robot can rotate on its base, and has a long double-ended arm, with a gripper at each end. The arm can articulate on the robot body, like a see-saw. At the first station, the robot is equipped with a mechanical gripper to pick the panel from the press, but the next three robots are equipped with suckers. To move the panel from one press to another, the arm first extends into the press in a slightly raised position, and then articulates downwards to grip the panel. Then, it moves upwards a little, withdraws, and almost immediately rotates through 180° on its base, so that the panel is now near the next press. Afterwards, the robot arm extends, moves downwards, and deposits the panel in the next press. At the last station, a robot with a normal arm removes the panels from the press and places them in pallets. (Fig. 6.2)

These four robots replaced eight men and four 'iron hands' which are used in most plants to remove the panels from presses. Iron hands are not very reliable, and need some setting up for each panel – it is normal to change the dies to run a different pressing several times a week. Thus, the robots, which cost around £100,000, replaced a total of 16 men, and an annual net wages bill of £96,000. One complication with this installation is

Fig 6.2   Volkswagen robot handling panels between presses

that because the robot turns through 180° as it transfers the panel between presses, the dies at successive presses need to be installed the opposite way around – that is with edge that is nearest the rear of the first press nearest the front of the second press. Although this application seems successful, handling at presses is a rather specialised business, and generally, simpler devices that are attached to the press are preferred, even though two are needed instead of one robot. In this case, the robots were able to operate a 10s cycle, which is very fast.

In forging, a robot can be used either to transfer heavy and very hot workpieces between furnaces and forging presses, or to manipulate the workpiece at one press. Generally, robots with six axes of freedom are considered best for this job, and of course, in many cases, a capacity of 50–150kg is needed. But experience in forges operated by Alfa Romeo in Italy shows that universal robots can be used effectively for workpieces of at least 4–5kg, so long as there are three passes at the press. The payback period is fairly long, at three to four years, but if the robot can be organised to work continuously through the shifts, it can show an increase in productivity of 30%. The reason for this is that the working conditions are so bad, with the heat and weight of the workpieces, that the workers normally need frequent breaks. Nevertheless, to improve the effectiveness of the robot in the forge, more rapid acceleration and deceleration is needed. Thus, complex acceleration/deceleration curves, which can be developed relatively easily, are essential.

One interesting device for forging is the 'soft' gripper developed by the French Forgers' Association. The gripper releases the workpiece slightly as the ram descends, so that the workpiece can be formed more easily into the dies, and to prevent the shock of the impact affecting the robot. The gripper closes again as the ram is raised, and since the control system monitors the position of the ram, synchronization is precise. In addition, a television camera monitors the position of the workpiece.

In diecasting shops, robots are now used extensively to remove castings from the diecasting machine – the process being mechanised with automatic ladling of the aluminium or zinc into the machine, and with automatic lubrication. Because the robot unloads the casting, dips it into a quenching tank, and then places it into a trimming press, this is a good application. But for very small components, it is simpler to eject the casting from the machine into a quenching trough below, a drag conveyor transferring the casting to a pallet. One of the pioneers in the use of robots to handle castings weighing 5–10kg was Teksid, the Fiat foundry subsidiary in Italy. In 1974, it started to install 10 Unimates, and these were used mainly to handle products with a cast weight of 10kg. (Fig. 6.3)

The robot withdraws the casting from the machine, which involves extending the arm, pivoting towards the casting, grasping it, and pivoting back, before withdrawing. Then, it dips the casting in a tank of water to cool it, releasing the casting. The robot regrips the casting, and feeds it into a trimming press, from which the casting is ejected automatically. In this case, one operator was retained for a group of machines, to do some trimming, while controlling the number of parts produced, and ensuring that the holding furnace remained full of molten aluminium. The direct advantage of the use of robots was that productivity increased by an average of 35% in the foundry, and by 47% in some cases. A subsidiary advantage was that owing to more consistent operation, die life improved, with the result that the time lost in changing dies was reduced from 10% to 5% of productive time. Allowing for start-up time, and diechanging, utilisation of the robots averaged 82%.

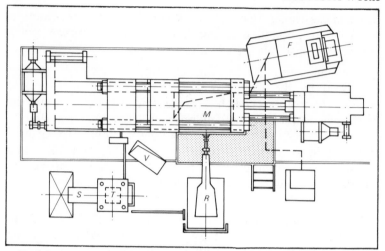

Fig 6.3   Arrangement of a Unimate robot at a diecasting machine at Teksid. R, robot; M, machine; F, holding furnace with automatic ladle; V, cooling tank; T, trimming press; S, chute

Mossner of Munich installed one Unimate 2000 robot at a 700 tonne diecasting machine, and found that a lot of time was saved after the robot was programmed to lubricate the dies – in fact, the robot was programmed to duplicate the movements of a diecaster. Subsequently, three robots were installed, operating on a 90s cycle, including the 30s during which the component was cast. The diecasting shop was planned to operate on three shifts. Therefore, the three robots, supervised by one man/shift, could do the work of three men/shift, thus reducing the manning level by six.

In Japan, Nippondenso, a maker of automotive electrical equipment, built its own robots for handling at diecasting machines. These are of the cylindrical coordinate type, with three principle axes of movement, and one at the wrist. The robot removes the casting, quenches it, and inserts it in the trimmer, depositing the sprue and riser, which it is grasping, into a bin. As in the Teksid application, the trimmer ejects the casting into a pallet. When the robots were first installed, they took 45s to carry out this cycle of operations, but with development of the software and of the robots themselves, the cycle time was reduced to 30s. Thirteen robots are used, one to a machine, and only three men are needed – previously, there was one man at each machine. (Fig. 6.4, 6.5)

Fig 6.4   Nippondenso robot removing a pair of castings from a high
pressure diecasting machine

Fig 6.5   To extract diecastings a long reach is frequently required

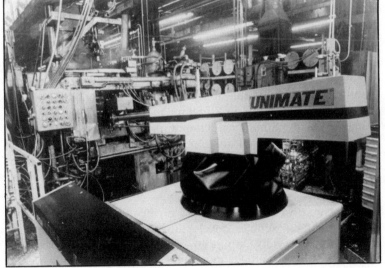

Several suppliers of foundry equipment have produced robots for use in diecasting shops, and these are generally simpler than the Unimate. However, because the robot needs to remove the casting, and then go through quenching and trimming, a complex set of movements is needed. Some foundry managers are looking for more dexterous robots, so that the casting can be removed more quickly. Then, there is the question of whether the lubrication spray system should be carried by the robot. Certainly, a robot could spray with far more precision than the systems in use at present, and because the procedure is in software, and does not involve any hardware changes, downtime at die changes could be cut. In any case, the diecasting business is one where it is difficult to recruit and retain labour, so the use of robots is certain to increase dramatically, with good gains in productivity.

In plastics injection mouldings, the robots in use are more like programmable arms attached to the machine than robots. Once a machine is installed, it carries out the same basic movements irrespective of the parts being produced. The only changes are to the cycle, which is controlled by the machine, and the gripper. But this is another area where the 'robot', if the arm deserves such a name, has quickly become dominant. Indeed, unless the mouldings are very difficult to remove, all injection moulding machines should be equipped with robotic arms, which are likely to be much more cost-effective than free-standing robots.

NC machines

Handling workpieces at NC machine tools is another application that has aroused a lot of interest. Kawasaki Heavy Industries mounted one Unimate robot on a slide giving about 30m of movement so that it could traverse between two lines of NC machines in a cell in a factory in Japan several years ago, but this was a rather cumbersome installation giving doubtful advantages. However, Fanuc, the Japanese maker of numerical controllers and small machine tools, devised a range of robots specially for handling at NC machines, and these have proved cost-effective.

The Fanuc M series robots are of the cylindrical co-ordinate type, the first machines developed being freestanding devices. They are generally equipped with grippers developed by Yamatake-Honeywell designed to grip workpieces of different

Fig 6.6   A Unimate mounted on a slide to service a large group of
machine tools at Kawasaki Heavy Industries

sizes without the need to change the gripper. For example, one gripper is suitable for workpieces of 20–118mm outside diameter. The Model 1, and Model 3 are five-axis machines, and the Model 1 can rotate on its base through 300°. There is 500mm vertical movement, and 500 or 800mm extension of the arm, while the gripper can usually carry 10kg.

In its first application, Fanuc installed 12 robots in the dc servo motor machine shop, with nine allotted to one NC lathe each, two serving three NC lathes, and one serving four NC machines. The number of machines served by each robot was dictated partly by space, and partly by the cycle times – the NC lathes generally operate on short cycle times. To reduce manning levels, Fanuc developed carousel storage units which were placed alongside the lathes. On each carousel were a number of pins on which the workpieces were carried, and as the NC machine started a new cycle, so the carousel was indexed around one position to present a new workpiece to the robot. Each carousel was designed to hold enough workpieces for about three hours operation. (Fig. 6.7)

The robot has a double gripper, so that it can pick up a new

Fig 6.7   A robot working at a lathe with workpieces arranged on a table

workpiece from the carousel, move into the machine, pick up the finished workpiece, and then spin the gripper round 180° so that the new workpiece can be installed with the minimum downtime. Thus, maximum machine tool utilisation could be obtained. Also, while in the machine, an air gun on the robot blows away the swarf. When the robot arm withdraws from the machine, it deposits the workpiece on the carousel, picks up a new workpiece, and is ready to start again. The robot working at the four machining centres was handling two different workpieces of quite different size. In addition, the robot also changes the tool on one machine prior to a boring operation.

Since the machines were equipped with automatic compensation for tool wear, Fanuc was able to operate the machines unmanned through the lunch break, and also for up to four hours of overtime – this plant operated on one shift only. In fact, during the overtime, one supervisor remains. In addition to this boost to productivity, the robots replaced 13 men. But in Fanuc's Fuji factory, eight robots load NC lathes in a plant operated for three shifts, the third shift being completely unmanned – apart from a computer operator in the control room. In this case, the eight robots are probably equivalent to 10 men.

One small company that demonstrated the advantages of

Fanuc robots at machine tools is Miyanaga, a maker of twist drills, principally for concrete. A small Japanese company, it employs about 200 people. It decided to start machining shanks and cups itself instead of relying on sub-contractors, and so invested £2,500,000 in a new plant. Small bar auto turret lathes are used in one half of the shop, and a number of lathes in the other half. Miyanaga installed 11 Fanuc robots, eight at one small NC lathe each, and three each serving two larger lathes. The small lathes work on cycles of about three minutes and the larger machines average 20 minutes.

Generally, the robots are arranged in groups, facing outwards to their lathes. But rather than use expensive carousel buffer stores, Miyanaga has installed a number of wooden tables to carry the workpieces. In each table, about 80 holes are drilled. These are equally spaced in a square pattern, and each serves as a location for one unmachined workpiece. The robot is programmed to pick these in sequence. After it has been machined, the workpiece is deposited in a bin by the robot. However, to load the tables, the men must place workpieces in an area through which the robot gripper is moved. This is a potentially dangerous situation. Nevertheless, this is a very simple set-up, automatic compensation for wear allowing almost unmanned operation. In addition, if tool wear exceeds 0.3mm, the machine stops automatically – and this feature takes care of tool breakage.

Miyanaga operates the factory on two shifts, with 12 men on the day shift, and only two on the night shift. The workers on the night shift load the bar autos and tables only, whereas the men on the dayshift are responsible for maintenance, inspection and other ancillary jobs. What's more the nightshift workers are 'casual labourers' earning about 60% of the wages of the regular workers. Thus, it is not surprising that this is a profitable installation, saving Miyanaga about £1 million a year in the cost of turned parts. In this case the 11 robots are equivalent to about 12 men, saving about £80,000 a year in 1981, to give a payback period of about four years.

In Sweden, robots are used widely in machine shops, one notable user being Saab-Scania, the vehicle manufacturer. In most cases, the robot serves more than one machine, and the payback period in four early applications varied from six months to 2.2 years. In one case, two robots were incorporated in a line where mainshafts for truck gearboxes were machined. Five different shafts, weighing 5–8kg, and 148–216mm in length, are produced at a rate of 100,000 a year on two shifts. The robots were installed in two areas: one, where complex handling was needed; and in the centre of a machining cell.

The line was arranged in three sections, the first a straight section with two lathes and two gear shapers, with an automatic loading/unloading system and a conveyor between them. At the end of that line is a robot, serving a drilling machine and a washer. Then, a conveyor transfers workpieces to a machining cell with one robot and four machines arranged in a circle. (Fig. 6.8, 6.9)

The first robot is an ASEA Electrolux Senior, which picks the shaft from the second gear shaper, and transfers it to the drilling machine. At this station, the robot holds the shaft during drilling, then turns the shaft over so that another hole can be drilled. When the drilling is finished, the robot places the shaft in a washing machine.

At the cell, an Asea robot picks the workpiece from a magazine and transfers it in sequence through milling, deburring, shaving, and stamping operations. Finally, the robot places the shaft in a pallet.

Fig 6.8   Handling robot built onto an NC machine with a carousel buffer store nearby

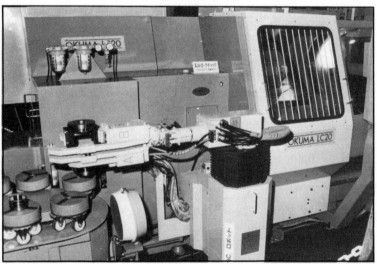

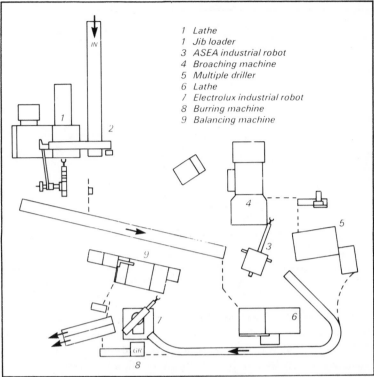

1 Lathe
1 Jib loader
3 ASEA industrial robot
4 Broaching machine
5 Multiple driller
6 Lathe
7 Electrolux industrial robot
8 Burring machine
9 Balancing machine

*Fig 6.9   Arrangement of two robots in a machining cell for transmission
drive flanges at Saab-Scania*

This system operates to a cycle of about 2min 30s, and with
the conveyors, reduced the manning level by four men/shift.
Quite a substantial conveyor system was needed, and there is a
buffer store and a number of magazines. Thus, the cost of the
investment was divided between the various sections as follows:

*Capital cost of Automated Handling
Proportion needed for Robot and Associated Equipment:*

Item	Proportion, %
One Senior robot	11
One ASEA robot	46
Conveyors, turntables, magazines, and ancillaries	17
Adaptation of machines	26

The payback period was 2.2 years, which is a short period for
parts such as these, which remain in production for many years.

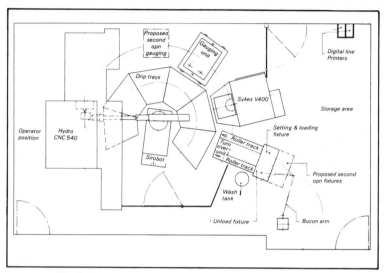

Fig 6.10   Layout of machining cell at British Aerospace

In one of its latest installations, Saab-Scania has installed three cells of machine tools, each loaded by its own robot, to machine flanges for universal joints at a nominal rate of 70,000 parts a year on two shifts. In the first cell, an Electrolux Senior robot loads and unloads at a lathe. In the second cell, an ASEA IRb 60 60kg robot handles between a broach, multiple drill and lathe. In the third cell, another Electrolux Senior robot handles between the conveyor, a burring machine and balancer. However, a special-purpose arm is used to place the workpiece in the balancer, although the robot removes it. In this case, the three robots and three lengths of conveyor do the work of 10 men. Total investment in the handling equipment was £150,000, giving a payback period of less than two years. (Fig. 6.10)

ZF, the German transmission manufacturer has produced many robots for use in its own machine shops, and for sale. It too has concentrated on using robots designed specially for handling at cells, to minimize investment. Even where a robot is used to handle between a buffer store and gear hobbing and gear chamfering machines, it can be cost-effective. (Fig. 6.11)

Ancillary handling

However, in many applications, a much simpler handling device is adequate. Therefore, the Institute of Production

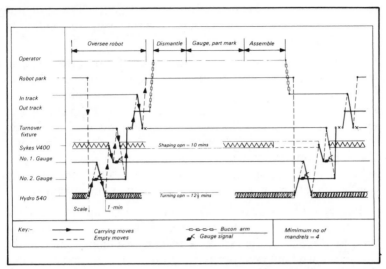

Fig 6.11   Timing sequences at the British Aerospace machining cell

Automation, (IPA), Stuttgart has devised a simple NC loader to handle between magazines of parts and an assembly robot or some machines. It was developed because the engineers at IPA felt that most robots were far too complicated and expensive for handling. Certainly, for palletising, which this loader has been found to perform adequately, a universal robot is usually unnecessary. In foundries and forges, there are many ancillary handling jobs where the full flexibility of a robot cannot be used, but where grippers that can handle different parts are needed. Again, something between a robot and hard automated handling device is needed. For very small objects, a pneumatic pick-and-place robot is sufficient.

The robot is of the portal or gantry type, and it has only two axes of freedom – it can slide across a pair of rails, or it can move up and down vertically. There is a simple rack and pinion drive, so the machine can be built or adapted to suit any length of traverse needed. In addition the device could be supplied with extra slides for manual movement at right angles to the rails. This would be used if the device were to be moved to a different machine. Magazines are fed to the working area of the loader along a continuously moving conveyor, and are held stationary by a mechanical stop. The loader then picks and places the workpieces as necessary. Also included is a bar code reader, so that the loader can be sent to the correct pallet. The system is under microcomputer control and is an inexpensive solution to flexible handling. It can operate to a cycle of 15s.

In the future, handling robots, apart from those used at special applications, such as in diecasting foundries, are likely to be simplified. For example, many machine tool companies are now producing robot arms that are fitted on to the machine, and which can load/unload between machine and carousel buffer store. In some cases, the movements are simple, and in others they are complex. But to gain a good return on the use of a robot in a machining cell, it needs to be able to operate very quickly, and to be able to handle at more than one machine.

For example, since the robot can control the operations of the machine tools, it might be most economic to use one fast robot with long reach at the centre of several machines – and all the machines need not necessarily be working in the same cell. Each machine could then be equipped with a very simple arm which merely loaded and unloaded the workpiece. This could be a pneumatic device with just two axes of freedom. It could either drop the workpiece on to an intermediate holder, for the robot to move on to the next station, or it could wait for the robot to take it from its gripper. The robot could control all the machines. Alternatively, the small cell approach, with two or three machines together, is effective.

For machining very large components, a completely different system, based on cranes that are really robots, or air pallets with similarly flexible controls are more likely to be effective. In any event, the key with handling is to use the simplest device possible but with a flexible control system – unless the robot is to be used as a manipulator in which case an advanced robot is essential.

CHAPTER SEVEN
Arc welding

EVENTUALLY, robots will be used for almost all arc welding, but in the past, the high cost of the robot has deterred most potential users. After all, whereas a set of CO_2 welding equipment costs about £1,000, a welding robot costs about £30,000 – and usually an operator is still needed for one or maybe two robots. The reason that arc welding robots have been so expensive is that most have been universal machines with five or six axes of freedom. Two types have predominated: the Cartesian coordinate and jointed arm types. Some of the Cartesian coordinate machines have massive structures, with the welding gun on a column hanging down from a gantry. A positioning table, which can be rotated in one or two planes, is used to carry the workpiece – overall, a costly set of equipment. The jointed arm robot, typified by the ASEA and Yaskawa (Fig. 7.1) machines, is very dexterous, with a lot of movement, and so it too is costly.

Against that however, arc welding shops need robots which can actually weld faster than a man. Although welding is a skilled job, working conditions are very bad; not only must the operator peer at the weld through a heavily tinted glass – his eyes are always in danger – but there is quite a lot of noise from the arc. In addition, there are the fumes to contend with. Then, arc welding shops are invariably dirty, with each man working in a curtained booth, a situation that thwarts attempts to introduce flowline systems. Obviously, in these circumstances, the welders are entitled to take breaks, and are likely to stop for short periods between breaks as well. Owing to the poor working conditions, people are not keen to train to become welders. The training schemes tend to be out of date, encompassing a long period and all types of welding. Such skills

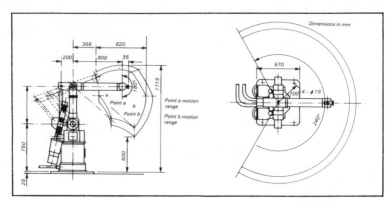

Fig 7.1   A typical arc welding robot, in this case the Yaskawa L10 machine

are not needed in most production shops, so the welding robot, preferably backed up by men who can do some arc welding, must be the solution of the future.

Of course, where one large assembly is produced in big volumes, rows of automatic welders can be used with a shuttle transport system. But these are usually housed in long tunnels, and since the automatic machines have limited capability, many are needed. If one breaks down, a long stoppage is almost inevitable, as the line must be stopped while the maintenance men go into the tunnel to sort things out.

Before arc welding robots can be installed to give an improvement in productivity, some extra jigs are needed. (Fig. 7.2) The most common method is to use a turntable, with the robot on one side, and the operator loading and unloading on the other. Universal clamping systems can be used in a jobbing shop, but usually special purpose jigs are carried on the table. In this set up, the turntable is controlled – and sometimes operated – manually, so it is not expensive. There is a curtain across the middle of the turntable. (Fig. 7.3)

But how can a £30,000 machine, replacing one man, be made economic? Of course, it depends on the welding and the way the shop is organised. Generally, the robot is best for fairly simple welds, especially when there are many in one assembly. Where the welds are long and complicated the robot may not be faster because it may need to turn one long weld into many short ones, reorientating itself before starting each section of the weld. Where welds are repetitive the robot is likely to do a better job,

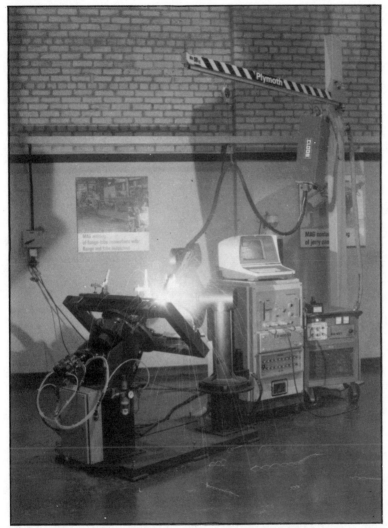

Fig 7.2   Special fixtures are needed for arc welding work

especially if flowline handling equipment can be used on the line.

But even where welds are long, the robot gives an unexpected bonus, as it does in so many other applications: it can weld faster than a man. ESAB, the welding company that works in conjunction with ASEA on arc welding robot applications, found that with robot welding it is possible to weld at a higher current and traverse the welding gun more quickly than normal.

Fig 7.3   Turntables can be operated both manually and automatically

For example, materials that can be welded manually at 70cm/ min, can be welded at 250cm/min by robot – 3.5 times faster. That alone can give a big boost to productivity.

Even so, some very big jobs, where accuracy is important, do not lend themselves to robot welding yet. The problem is that a lot of time is needed to set them up, whereas with manual welding, the operator just attaches a couple of clamps. With really effective sensors that can find the start of a weld, and follow the weld path without further manual interference, this situation will change.

Where there are many short welds, though, the situation is different. For example, Dahlstrom Manufacturing, New York, installed a Cincinnati Milacron T3 robot to weld up bases for computer main frames in lots of 35 to 75. This is a square structure of tubes, with three cross beams and a number of shorter reinforcements. For welding it was mounted on a simple jig with clamps, much of the welding equipment, including the reel of wire, being mounted on the robot itself. The manufacturing manager said that whereus manual welding of 44 welds, each about 50mm long, took 42 minutes, the robot could do the job in 12 minutes.

Why was there such a difference? Although there was about 2.2m of welding, the fact that there were 40-odd movements between welding increased the robot's advantage. The man has to decide in which sequence to do the welds, and he would probably move around the fixture as he welded, all of which takes time. Then, when he has finished welding, he has to check that he has in fact made all the welds. By contrast, the production engineers and a welder would spend some time refining the robot's process and movements, so that the job is done with the minimum of movements. Of course, the robot does not need to check that it has made all the welds, nor does it slow up towards the end of the day. Those differences add up to a cut in welding time of 70%. To boost output by an equal amount with manual welding, the company would have needed an extra 2.5 men, so clearly this was a cost-effective solution.

ESAB and ASEA have produced considerable data to show how their welding robots improve productivity, usually in conjunction with simple fixtures. For example, Fantic Motor, the Italian company, adopted ASEA robots for arc welding small motor cycle frames. Now 90% of the welds of the frame are made by robot, and the manager claimed productivity had been tripled, with an output of 110 frames/shift. Dowdeswell Engineering, a British manufacturer of agricultural equipment, claims robots are three times faster than manual welding.

Specific examples back up this claim. Sperry New Holland, Belgium, introduced a robot to weld up a large gear casing, 720 x 420 x 400mm, which weighs 110kg. The plates were 16mm thick. A total of 7.3m of welding in 32 sections, was done on each. With manual welding, the job took 69 minutes; by robot it took 33 minutes. Broderna Hammarstedt Verkst, AB, Sweden, demonstrated the advantages on a much smaller and thinner part – a car seat frame weighing 4kg and made of plate 0.9–3mm thick. On each frame there are 22 welds, with a combined length of 550mm. With manual welding, the job took 2.4 minutes, and with the robot 1.5 minutes. A trolley tray, with 44 welds, averaging 35mm in length, was welded in 10.8 minutes by a welder of Tomado, Holland. The robot did the job in 4.5 minutes. In this case, the metal was 1.5mm thick. All these examples show that with simple jigging, robots can bring dramatic improvements in productivity.

With improved positioning, the job can be speeded up further, so ASEA has developed a number of special workpiece manipulators. One is designed for orbital welding around drums and cylinders; another is a turntable for handling two workpieces for orbital welding. A third manipulator, also a turntable, carries a pair of fixtures that can be rotated, and which themselves can rotate the workpiece. These devices will improve the productivity of robot welding, but not in a dramatic way.

However, a dramatic improvement in cost-effectiveness has been made by Yamaha Motors, the Japanese motor cycle manufacturer. It did so by designing and installing a large number of simpler, cheaper robots and operating them for three shifts a day. The robots are used to weld up motor cycle frames.

It spent about 10 years developing its robots into effective tools for arc welding. Then, between 1980 and 1982, the company installed about 100 robots to increase the amount of mechanized arc welding of frames from 30 to 80%. Apart from one or two machines, these were all designed by Yamaha, and are much simpler and cheaper than the universal arc welding robot produced by robot manufacturers.

These robots are concentrated in a small factory that covers an area of 21,000m². The motor cycle frames being welded are made from a number of steel tubes and pressings with wall thicknesses of around 2mm, at a rate of 150,000 a month. Most of these welds are short, and many are at junctions of round tubes.

Over the years, Yamaha has switched from a Cartesian co-ordinate column robot to a polar type and an overhead Cartesian co-ordinate type. This overhead type consists of a carriage from which a column carrying the welding gun hangs down. The carriage can move longitudinally through about 1.5m, laterally through about 0.5m on slides, and the column can extend to lower the gun to the workpiece. In addition, the gripper can rotate the welding gun.

The polar type robot has a 900mm long arm which can pivot through only 100° horizontally on a short pillar. The arm can articulate through about 30° vertically, and can extend telescopically 600mm. In practice, the robot can weld within an envelope about 600mm high by 600mm long – in the direction along the arm – and 900mm wide. As on the overhead robot, the wrist houses a motor which can rotate the welding gun through

Fig 7.4   Yamaha arc welding robot increases productivity of motor cycle frames

270°. Both these robots have only four axes of movement, and the amount of travel is deliberately restricted to obtain a simple but stiff mechanism and rapid operation. (Fig. 7.4)

The main problem in installing the robots was to provide sufficiently accurate jigs. With the thinner tubes, an accuracy of ±0.02mm was necessary. In other places an accuracy of ±0.05mm was sufficient. Wherever robots replace manual welding, more accurate jigs, and often more accurately produced pressings are needed; the man compensates for the poor fit of the panel by forcing or by bending the panel into position. At present, robots cannot do this. At Yamaha, the combination of CO_2 welding and the relatively thick tubes or panels meant that distortion during welding was not the problem it can be with panels of 0.8–1.5mm thickness.

The overhead type robots are used mainly for simple welds. Therefore, in one line, six of these robots, attended by two men, weld up steering head assemblies. The assembly consists of the tubular steering head which is welded to a pair of channel section pressings to produce a T-shape box section. The assembly is approximately 300mm long by 100mm deep by 50mm wide. (Fig. 7.5)

*Fig 7.5   Overhead robots are used also at Yamaha for simple jobs
requiring a large working envelope*

To supplement these robots, there are special fixtures and
removal arms. The fixture is a plate mounted on a turntable
which can rotate on horizontal spindles. There is a large hole in
the plate through which the assembly can pass. Beneath the
fixture is a tray carried on an arm. The operator loads the
assembly in the fixture manually, and as soon as he presses the
start button, a pair of curtains is automatically drawn across to
prevent glare. Then, the fixture rotates as necessary to present
the assembly to the welding gun. When the welds have been
made, the fixture releases the workpiece which falls through the
hole on to the tray below. The tray is rotated so that the
workpiece can be removed later, and the curtains are opened
automatically.

In one or two places, the robot cannot make the weld easily,
so the operators make a few short welds afterwards. In addition,
alongside the last robot is a fine boring machine, in which the
operator machines the steering head before placing it in a pallet.

Most of the polar robots are used to weld up frame sub-
assemblies or complete frame assemblies. Generally, the welds
are very short – 25–50mm is typical – but there are many of
them. In one line, eight robots are arranged in a circular path to
weld frames, and in another case, 10 robots are arranged in a

*Fig 7.6   Robots arranged in rows carry out a sequence of welds on
tubular frames*

straight line – the layout was dictated by the space available. In
both cases, three men are employed on each line, to load the
workpieces into the jigs, and to make some welds. (Fig. 7.6)

Three types of fixture are used: in a few cases there is a turntable fixture with a man welding on one side and a robot welding
on the other; in many others, the fixture can turn through 180
deg automatically, so the robot can weld both sides of the frame;
and in the third type the frame is held in one position only, with
the robot attacking from that side only.

At the turntable fixture, the operator first loads the tubes and
pressings, and then tack welds them in position. Before the turntable rotates, he knocks the reinforcing panel into position with a
hammer – that is the sort of job that is often needed with a
welded structure, but which a robot cannot do at present. In
most other applications, the operator stands at a bench opposite
the robot, and in addition to loading and unloading, completes a
few welds. These are always short welds, which can be made
without any jigging. Nearly all the robots are equipped with
automatic curtains which are closed before the robot starts
welding, a simple and neat solution to one problem in arc
welding by robot.

Despite the flexibility of the robots, one overhead line is used for one type of steering head assembly only. But each of the other lines is used to produce three or four different assemblies. There are two types of fixtures: some have clamps for two different assemblies, but in other cases, the jigs are changed completely. This is done every other day. 'It usually takes 30–40 minutes to change the jigs, but we are trying to reduce this to 20 minutes,' said the production manager.

Cycle times are generally about two minutes, and each robot makes 30–40 'welds' per cycle. In fact, the actual number of welds on the assembly may appear to be only 15–20, but to allow the robot to make the welds without the need for too much dexterity, one weld is often broken down into two or three short runs. 'For example, we divide the circular weld at a joint between two tubes, where a full 360° weld is needed, into three welds,' said the manager. These tubes are usually 20–50mm diameter.

To make the robots pay, and to meet the increasing demand for its motor cycles, Yamaha operates the Hamakita plant, where the robots are installed, on three shifts, employing 200 people as direct labour. Overall, there are 145 Yamaha robots in the plant made up of 135 polar machines and 10 overhead units. On average, one robot replaces half a man per shift. If the welding is simple, then one robot replaces a man, but at the other extreme, a robot may only replace one-third of a man. The robots are therefore doing the work of about 220 people, so the payback period is probably less than two years. Since Yamaha built the robots for its own use, it has not revealed their cost, but if bought from a supplier, each robot would probably cost about £16,000–18,000. Yamaha's costs are likely to have been 30% lower.

The key to the success of this application is that the robots were made as simple as possible to keep their price down, while the awkward welds are left to the operators. In addition, the fact that the robots are operated for 24 hours a day reduces the payback period significantly. Like the other smaller installations, Yamaha's experience indicates that current robots can be used to boost productivity and quality of arc welding.

Sensing developments

The key to the widespread use of robot welding in jobbing shops, for lots of one to 100 is quicker teaching and improved sensing. Ideally, the robot should be able to do everything a man can do: read the drawing, pick the parts up, put them in the correct orientation, clamp them together and weld them. In other applications, the robot needs only to pick the parts up, put them in a fixture, and then weld. Of course, these jobs may not all be done by one robot. For example, for one-off jobs, the 'drawing' and assembly orientation could be stored in a central computer, and fed to the controller of a handling robot, which might act as the welding robot's mate, assembling and clamping the parts together on a pallet at a separate station.

To make its welds, the robot would need to be programmed as now, but would also need to be able to sense the position of the assembly, and identify the starting point of the weld with some precision. Vision is normally seen as the answer here, with the robot finding its way to the assembly, and precisely following the weld paths with its eyes. But the use of delicate cameras and complicated controllers is not necessarily the best solution. Indeed, it is possible that some conventional sensors can do the job. Certainly once the robot finds the approximate position of the weld, the exact position can be tracked down by existing sensors. Then, some methods of finding the actual position of the weld path, which may be slightly different from that expected are already available. (Fig. 7.7)

Fig 7.7.   Arc welding robots can be programmed for (top) straight line interpolation and (bottom) circular interpolation

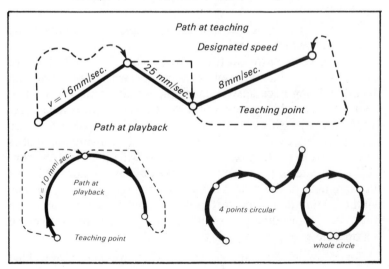

In small welding shops, where the men regard themselves as craftsmen, and are suspicious of electronics, the programming method involving a 'teachbox' is too complicated. It is also too slow for many small batches, even though recent systems are much quicker than old ones. To overcome this problem, Trallfa has adopted its 'lead-through' teaching system for its new TR–4000 welding robot. In this system, the operator merely holds the welding gun, and moves it through the welding operation. This is a very rapid process, and is likely to be copied. Certainly, it makes the robot much easier to use by operators.

There are already control systems that allow a curve to be followed after only three points have been taught, and sensing systems that can find the start of the weld, so long as the welding wire is within about 15mm of the correct position. These sensors, the first of which was developed by Shin Meiwa in Japan, are intended to allow for differences in jigging. The principle is that the welding wire is used as a probe, and is moved around near the actual weld point, making error corrections after each movement. For example in a simple 90° corner weld, the wire is moved in until it strikes a metal wall. Then, it is moved back a short distance at 90° to that wall, turned through 90° and moved until it strikes the other wall. By making error corrections, the distance from the corner of the V is reduced in steps until the wire is at the correct starting point. This is a slow process, taking 20–30s, but it can be used for butt joints as well as corner joints.

Yaskawa has also developed a simple electrical sensing system with which the robot can follow the weld path precisely once it has been started at the correct point. This is designed for plates with a thickness of 4.5mm upwards, this minimum thickness being necessary because the welding gun weaves as it welds. As the weld weaves, so the electrical current is measured. If the gun is passing exactly down the middle of the weld path, the current at each end of the weave will be identical. If it is diverging from the true path, the currents will differ, and the controller will alter the position of the welding gun accordingly. At the beginning of the weld Yaskawa claims the gun need be only within 20mm of the correct position, and that the robot can follow curved welding paths without being programmed to do so – a time saver in programming.

For example, if an approximately U-shape section is welded

to an end plate, teaching of the robot is far simpler than normal. In the case cited by Yaskawa, there are three changes of direction – small angles – in the first of the three walls. At the end, there is a near right-angle, and in the second and third wall are some curves. Without the sensor, at least 13 points would need to be taught with CP control, and more with PTP. In this case, only eight points had to be taught. The sensor adds about £4,500 to the cost of the robot, but it is likely to pay for itself in reduced programming time and supervision where small lots are produced. Since the robot will always follow the welding path correctly, less precise jigging can also be used than with conventional robots.

However, the age of vision sensing for arc welding is almost here, although the systems developed so far can be used to find the weld path prior to welding only – until now, a system that can overcome the interference of the light from the arc itself has not been found, even though many such systems are under development. Unimation and Kawasaki, in a joint project, and Mitsubishi Electric have devised simple systems exploiting aspects of vision.

The Unimation/Kawasaki system consists of a sensing unit, an area image detector, and an image processor. In the sensing unit is an optical slit pattern projector and a bundle of optical fibres, which transfer the image to a remote image detector and processor. To overcome interference from shadows cast by factory lighting, a bright projector is used. In operation, the robot picks up the sensing unit, and traverses the predetermined weld path. Errors in tracking are noted, and the controller alters the proposed weld path accordingly. Then, the robot returns the sensor to the stand, picks up the welding gun, and makes the weld. To improve accuracy, during the sensing path, the projector projects a slit of light at 45° to the workpiece, while the detector lens 'reads' this at 90° to the workpiece. The image is transferred to the image processor, and the actual image is compared with a 'shifted template' image. Many shifted templates are generated after teaching, and one of these is overlapped with the image from the sensor to determine the offset of each position along the weld.

Unimation recommends that one sensor is used with up to four arc welding robots, each robot picking up the sensor and using it as necessary. It is claimed that the sensing pass is very quick, taking only 10% of the welding pass, so that the increase in cycle time is small. Since the sensor costs about 20% as much as a robot, it is claimed that the ratio of one sensor to four robots gives a better return on investment than the use of robots without the sensor.

In the Mitsubishi Electric system, an infra-red light-emitting diode (led) directs a beam of light at a scanning mirror which oscillates at a constant rate to scan the beam across the workpiece. As with the Unimation/Kawasaki system, there needs to be a discernible joint – either a V-notch, corner or lap joint – for the system to function effectively. The led and mirror are housed in the sensing unit along with the lens and image detector. During the scanning operation, the robot traverses the joint to be welded, and the actual pattern is compared with an indicator which shows where the centre of the path should be. (Fig. 7.8, 7.9) (Fig. 7.10)

To reduce cost and to speed up image processing, a two-dimensional lateral photoeffect diode is used as the area sensing device instead of a camera. It is a dual-axis position sensitive detector providing continuous information on the position of the movement of a spot of light on the detector. Unlike a camera, the screen is not divided into pixels, so the position of the spot can be detected without processing.

For the system to be effective the sensor needs to be 70–110mm from the workpiece and so it is carried on the robot arm. The scanner has a 20mm wide path, so the robot needs to

Fig 7.8   Configuration of a visual sensor system for weld gun guidance

Fig 7.9   Sensing image in optical pattern projection method

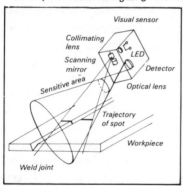

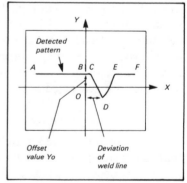

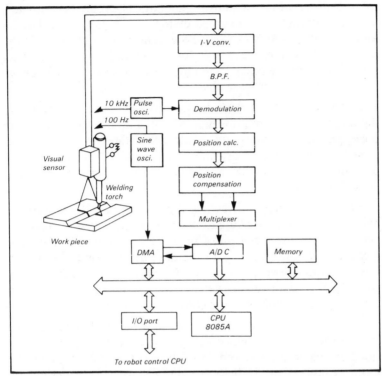

Fig 7.10   Schematic diagram of a signal processing unit

be preprogrammed to find the approximate start of the weld. Mitsubishi claims that the sensor can alter the weld path so that it is within 0.5mm of the correct position, which is sufficiently accurate for all but the thinnest sheets.

Whether these systems are practical factory equipment now is not certain, but they are much more practical than the use of costly and unreliable cameras for weld path sensing. Ultimately, of course, some system that can find and follow the weld path during the welding pass is needed, but that still seems to be well in the future.

Once vision is available, it offers all kinds of new concepts. For example, one problem with arc welding is that a man is usually needed to load and unload the workpieces from the jigs. Since the arc welding robot can be used to handle parts it can do its own loading – or a simple handling robot can do the job. Matsushita has developed a system in which the arc welding robot, with vision, does its own handling. The robot is combined with an automatically operated clamp on a table for welding; a separate table, which can be rotated and moved in the x and y axes; with a camera above it for orientation; and a chute to supply parts to the orientation table; there is also a conveyor on which completed parts are placed.

In operation, the part slides down the chute to the table and the camera detects the position and orientation. Responding to these positional signals, the controller rotates and moves the table as necessary to orientate the workpiece correctly and position it in the middle of the table. This operation happens almost instantly.

The robot, which carries a gripper, picks up the workpiece and places it on the welding table where is is gripped by a pair of clamps. Then the robot picks up a welding gun and welds the workpiece, following the path dictated by the controller, which has received information as to the part to be welded. After welding, the robot replaces the welding gun on its stand, and transfers the workpiece to the conveyor.

This is a neat installation in that the robot really does replace the operator. The ancillary equipment may be expensive, but since the camera is remote from the welding gun, it should be more reliable than if held by the robot. This experimental arrangement demonstrates that once vision comes along, the way in which robots can be used will expand rapidly. But the other applications show that already robots can give a boost to productivity in arc welding, because they can weld very quickly, they can move rapidly between welds, while their performance is consistent.

CHAPTER EIGHT
Spraying

UNLIKE most robot applications, paint spraying started in small workshops, and it is only relatively recently that large companies have become involved. But owing to the poor working conditions in paint booths, spraying needs to be automated. The large companies spraying objects such as cars can automate about 80% of the spraying with hard automation. But for the small company, spraying small parts in variety, the robot is the only alternative to an operator, who, incidentally, needs to be skilled to produce a good job.

Robot painting started when Ole Molaug, an engineer at a small company in Norway decided to try to produce a manipulator to spray wheelbarrows, trolleys and small implements. The reason for this decision was that the spray booth was a bottleneck. It still is a bottleneck in many companies and the reason is easy to see. The paint sprayers need to be fully covered in overalls, and they wear face masks. They work in a booth with the strong smell of solvents and droplets of paint in the atmosphere. Of course, it is a 'No smoking' area. In those unhospitable conditions the men have to spray to a consistent pattern and with a consistent pressure on the trigger to provide paint of the correct thickness. In addition, to spray large units like car bodies, the men have to bend double, and in some cases crawl inside.

In any event, Molaug devised a manipulator with hydraulic actuation. To teach the manipulator, the operator grasped the spraygun, and took it through the procedure he would use if he were spraying manually. The robot was a success, and in 1969, the company, called Trallfa, of Bryne, Norway, sold its first paint spraying robots. They were used to spray domestic baths, and were believed to be in use more than ten years later.

Meanwhile, Trallfa continued to spray its wheelbarrows and other parts by robot, but set up a fully-fledged robot division, which is reckoned to have cornered over 70% of the world's spray painting robot business.

The main reasons for the success of that machine were that it can be programmed easily by a painter, and with its jointed arm construction, it can spray most objects easily. Virtually all the other robots in use for spraying are of the jointed arm type, although Kobe Steel, Trallfa's licensee in Japan, has devised a small Cartesian co-ordinate machine that is claimed to be as flexible as a jointed arm robot. Recently, an 'elephant's trunk' wrist has been added to the Trallfa arm, to give greater versatility in spraying inside confined spaces, such as car bodies. (Fig. 8.1)

Fig 8.1   The motions of a typical spraying robot

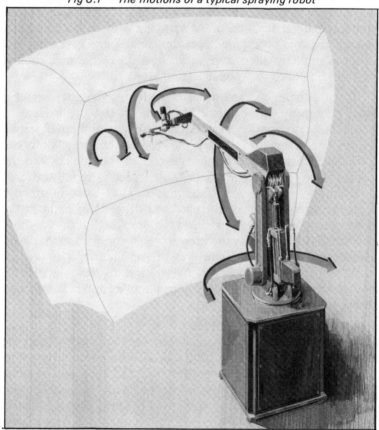

Fig 8.2   Trallfa robot with an 'elephant trunk' wrist spraying metal grilles

Normally, the robot sprays parts as they pass by on a conveyor, and so long as the parts are light, and do not tend to swing, not much in the way of special equipment is needed. However, an operator is needed to teach the robot, although once taught photoelectric cells and other devices can be used to tell the robot which parts are coming. (Fig. 8.2, Fig. 8.3)

Among the small companies that have switched to painting robots – in this case the Hall Automation Ramp – is Imhof-Bedco, a supplier of cabinets and enclosures for computer and telecommunications equipment. Three robots were installed, two to apply undercoats, and the third to apply a rough-textured spatter finishing material. The reason for installing these robots was that the paint shop was a bottleneck. After installation, it took the company about six months to get the robots spraying properly. It proved difficult to obtain consistent results with the thick paint used as a top coat. The solution was to install a device to ensure that the viscosity of the paint was maintained at a constant level. Of course, an operator could compensate accordingly, but the robot cannot. As a result of installing the robots, the company expects to be able to double turnover without increasing labour in the paint shop. The company has

Fig 8.3   Long-reach robot spraying inside van bodies

used 'robot painting' as a marketing aid, however, and claims that as a result, sales have increased significantly. Of course, the robots reduce manning levels as well.

In another plant, four rows of robots are used to spray plastics mouldings, approximately 1,500mm long by 200mm deep by 100mm. These are basically U-section, and are sprayed on the outside only. The first robot in each line applies the primer, and the other the colour coats. An interesting feature of this application is that one conveyor carries two rows of mouldings on opposite sides of a curtain, the rows of robots being installed opposite one another.

In the automotive industry, the attractions of using robots for painting are big, but so are the problems. Currently, most primer surfacers and top coats are applied by reciprocators at the sides and overhead the bodies, and these can spray 80% of the body with consistent results. There is a little more waste than might be the case with robots, and about four people are needed in each spray booth to spray the areas missed by the reciprocators – the front and rear, especially the lower portions, and the interior.

In theory robots do not require much ancillary equipment for spraying although it is important that the conveyor should not jerk or sway – the robot needs a target that is in the expected position. It is possible to stop the bodies for painting, but this presents problems in other areas, so generally the robot has to paint a moving body. The robot can be synchronised with the line, and systems can be included to ensure that if the line stops, the robot stops instantly – a tachometer on the conveyor can act as a sensor. However, if a conveyor is being stopped many times a day, the reasons for the stoppage should be investigated and rectified before the robots are installed.

It is also essential to decide whether the robot is to be serviced inside or outside the booth. If it is to be serviced outside the booth, it should be mounted on some form of moveable platform. Servicing costs are low, the Trallfa robot, for example, having a claimed uptime of over 98%, which is extraordinary, and which suggests that in many paint booths, the robot spends quite a lot of time waiting for work. Remote teaching arms, which allow the robot to be taught from outside the booth are available, but these are generally not as reliable as direct teaching inside the booth.

Robots are already being used in many car factories to apply underseal to the bottom of the car. This is a large area with reasonable access but it is an unpleasant job for any operator. Two robots can often do this job, but if the production rate is more than about 60 an hour – a line speed of above 4m/min – then four robots are normally used. To avoid overspray of the body sides, the conveyor must not swing.

The interior of small vans or cars with rear doors is also a good application with one robot usually doing the job of at least one man/shift. When undertaken manually the operator has to wear a hood with a respirator and a vizor which has to be cleaned regularly. In one application, a Trallfa robot with an ele-phant's trunk wrist is used to spray over 95% of the interior in 6min 30s. One robot applies the primer and another the top coat. The robot is carried on a beam and carriage, and at the beginning of the cycle is moved right inside the van to spray over the driver's compartment. Then, it is gradually withdrawn, finally spraying the door inner panels.

Powder coating is another good application since again powder spray booths are unpleasant; operators need to wear full protective clothing, including respirators. In addition, static electricity can cause explosions, and if there are no people in the booth, then the problem of static is virtually eliminated. In one application, four robots and reciprocators were used automatically to completely coat a body with primer. The robots spray the front and the rear ends, the door surrounds and door edges, inside the roof, the wheelarches and engine compartment. Each robot sprays for no more than 100s, and they also open and close the doors. These robots are synchronised with the conveyor, which was necessary since their arms delve right inside the car.

But the question facing the automotive industry is how to fully automate spraying? The reciprocators can cope with no more than 80% of the body surface, so robots are needed to fully automate the process. Currently, with reciprocators and robots, 95% of the welding can be automated, but according to DeVilbiss, the company that markets Trallfa robots in most countries for spraying, it is not normally possible to automate 100% with current equipment. DeVilbiss does say, though, that if the body could be sprayed without the doors being fitted – and most companies will not do that for fear of poor paint matching – then the elusive door shut areas around the pillars could be sprayed easily by robot.

This is one example of where practices need to be changed to exploit robots, and it is certainly not impossible to paint the bonnet, bootlid and doors off the body, on jigs going through the same booth as the body, even though it is heresy to most paint experts. While removal of these panels is one possible approach, it might be argued that if a robot was anything like as versatile as it was supposed to be, it should be able to paint anything a man can – after all, this is principally a question of dexterity and organisation.

As in many robot installations, there is a hidden bonus in 100% automation of spraying. In this case, it is in energy costs, since a large amount of air has to be pumped through the paint booth to allow the operators to breathe and to maintain a reasonable atmosphere there. In fact, a lot of energy is needed to move the air and dissipate the heat. In a typical spray booth, energy consumption is about 5 million W, and DeVilbiss calculates that in an unmanned booth, energy consumption could be cut in half – and 2.5 million W is a lot of energy to save.

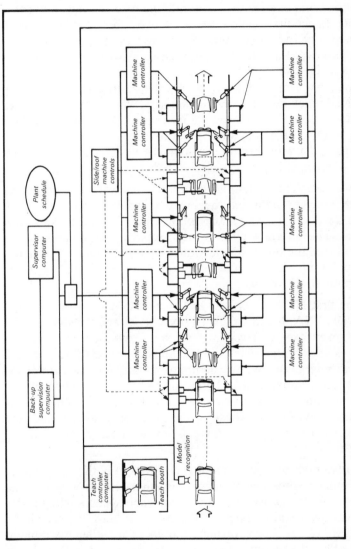

Fig 8.4   General Motors' NC painter system is under a supervisory computer. New bodies are programmed in a separate teach booth

That the solution is not easy can be gathered from the system General Motors has installed for 100% automated painting. It has devised a system called NC Painter, in which reciprocators and robots are used. At each section there is a set of reciprocators, one for the roof, and one for each side, and some robots. In the first section, there are two robot sets each side of the body; at the second there is one each side, and at the third there are two. Each robot set consists of two arms and one controller. (Fig. 8.4)

The main arm, used for spraying, is a seven-axis hydraulically actuated machine, while the second arm, which opens and closes the doors, has two main axes of movement. There is also a third axis, so that the hand can grip the fixture attached to the door. All the robot arms are on slides on the walls of the booth, and their movement is synchronised with the conveyor. (Fig. 8.5)

The complete system is under the control of a computer which receives data on the plant schedule. There is also a separate booth in which the robot arms are taught each new model. The program data is then stored in the computer. An optical recognition system identifies each body as it approaches the paint booth, and the program is called forth from the computer to the robots.

The first NC Painter was installed at GM's Doraville plant, Georgia, USA. It can handle all body styles and the robots, with their seven axes of freedom, can spray the inaccessible areas such as door hinge pillars and tailgate inner panel. Since the cars are fairly large the main structure terminates just forward of the passenger compartment. Therefore the bodies pass through the spray booths with the detachable front wings and the bonnet suspended on fixtures ahead of the main body, an arrangement that gives better access than is possible with cars having integral front ends.

Without doubt, people should be taken out of the spray booth to eliminate some bad working conditions and to improve the quality of paintwork. But to make robots economic in this application, some redesign of the robot or body is needed. As the GM system shows, opening the doors is not such a difficult job, while the robots can raise the bonnet and bootlid if necessary. Therefore, it seems only a matter of time before a better robot or system is designed to cope with the job more easily. The alternative is to redesign the body, or to alter

*Fig 8.5   Two views of the NC painter line. Top, the hydraulically driven
unit sprays body and front assemblies of station wagons. Below, for
interior painting the 'door operator' opens and closes car doors.*

practices, such as the way the doors are mounted during
spraying. After all, currently, plastics bumpers are sprayed in
body colour in quite separate paint plants from the bodies, so it
should not be impossible to paint the doors separately.

To simplify final assembly, Volkswagen-Audi is already
investigating the possibilities of building cars with separate
floors. This construction would lend itself to robot spraying.

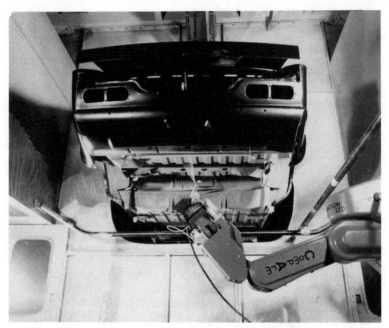

*Fig 8.6   Spraying the underneath of a car body. The robot is the Comp
Arm made by GEC*

Some robots could be installed beneath the line, with the bodies
passing overhead, and they could reach up inside the body to
spray the complete interior including those inaccessible door
shuts, wheelarches, boot and engine compartment. If this is too
radical a step, less major changes will almost certainly bring
improvements – but the implications are that if the full advantage is to be taken of robots for spraying complicated structures,
then both the spray booth and the product need to be altered.

CHAPTER NINE
Assembly – the biggest challenge

ASSEMBLY seems to be the most difficult job for a robot, yet successful robot assembly brings big rewards. Because assembly requires great dexterity, a lot of research effort has gone into visual and tactile sensing. Certainly if robots are expected to assemble in the same way as human beings, then very complex visual and tactile sensing are needed. In practice, however, many assembly jobs are simple, and robots can tackle these immediately. Other jobs can also be tackled by robot, so long as some modification to the procedure is made. Others seem to offer little hope for robot assembly however dexterous the robot may be, and however good its sensing may be.

Some applications are better left to hard automation: an example is assembly of very small parts, such as music boxes and electrical relays, which are produced to cycles of 1–3s. The assembly robot can just about manage a cycle of 3s, so it is unlikely to be cost-effective for this work. But that situation is likely to change; it is a question of when.

A product that demonstrates the advantages and limitations of robot assembly is the swash plate compressor used for vehicle air conditioning systems. It consists of a crankcase, split halfway along its length; a number of pistons with ball and cup contacts; the swash plate and shaft assembly; a number of bearing, valve plates and covers at each end. In some factories, automatic assembly is adopted for most jobs, the crankcase sub-assembly and end covers going down a line on a pallet. But prior to this, the pistons, and balls-and-cups are assembled manually to the swash plates. This is a job requiring great dexterity while the operator also has to choose from 20 grades of cups to obtain the necessary end-float. The operator has to hold the ball and cup assemblies in the piston, and then slide the swash plate between them. He then repeats the operation for the other pistons, holding the assembly together as he does so – it all takes about 30s. Then he places the assembly inside the crankcase. That job could conceivably be done by a robot, but it would be a very complex machine, with perhaps three arms, and several fingers on each gripper. Clearly, such a machine is a long way away.

In other areas of the line, though, hard automation seems to be very slow and ponderous. For example, at one station a bearing is pressed in, at another an oil seal is inserted, but then there are separate stations to turn the crankcase through 180° very slowly. A robot should be able to insert the seal and turn the crankcase through 180° in 25s, thus eliminating the need for one station. Then, a large oil seal, the valve plate and end cover are all installed manually in one quick cycle. A robot could do those jobs, although a special adaptor would be needed to handle the thin 100mm diameter 0–ring. But the robot should be able to install the parts as quickly as a man. Thus, in general, when compared with hard automation, the use of robots on assembly should reduce the number of stations needed.

When compared with manual assembly, though, the situation is very different. For example, all a man needs are a few small bins containing the parts he has to assemble – screws, washers, 0-rings, and rotors, for example. If the parts are jumbled up, the operator untangles them. If one is obviously the wrong size, he discards it. If the part is a tight fit but acceptable, he wiggles it into position a little slower than normal. If it slides in too easily, he rejects it. That may be a theoretical situation, but the point is that the existing robot cannot do those things. The parts must be supplied one by one from vibratory bowl feeders or by manually loaded chutes. If the robot can pick the part up it will do so and then try to force it into the housing, perhaps with disastrous results; if it is a loose fit, it does not react. This means that for robot assembly, parts must be produced with 'zero defects', and they must be correctly orientated; a daunting prospect in itself.

In addition the existing robots need a lot of ancillary equipment and precisely-made parts. Eventually, though, with force and visual sensors, the robot will be able to discard parts that are obviously not correct; and it will remove a part that slides in too easily, or which will not go in when the correct force is applied. What is more, it will be able to send back data to production control indicating which parts caused difficulties, and the drift in tolerances – human operators do not do that.

But that is all in the future. Even now, many parts can be assembled by robot easily and economically. As Hiroshi Makino, professor of Precision Engineering, Yamanashi University, Japan, and the designer of the Scara robot said: 'Almost all assembly is very simple – I would say 80%. It is a case of either inserting something vertically, screwing it down, or pressing it in. All of these can be automated quite easily.'

The Charles Stark Draper Laboratory, Massachusetts, USA, following an analysis of assembly arrived at a similar basic conclusion. It found that:

☐ 60% of the parts were inserted from one direction;
☐ 20% from the opposite direction;
☐ 10% at right angles to these directions;
☐ and 10% in other directions.

Thus the parts are stacked. From these data it was concluded that an arm with three degrees of freedom was sufficient for assembly. Typical jobs include: insertion and tightening of fasteners or pop rivets; pressing of bearings, pins and seals into housings; assembly of washers, contacts, rotors and stators; and the mounting of electronic components in circuit boards.

Typical products include consumer electronics and automotive parts which are replaced by newer designs every few years; parts such as gearboxes and electric motors and alternators, of which many different versions may need to be made on the same line, and almost anything cylindrical. So far, suitable assembly robots have been designed with relatively small capacities. One reason for this is that the assembly robot needs to be very precise in positioning, and this is more difficult to achieve with a robot that can carry 100kg, and move fairly long distances. (Fig. 9.1)

Currently, the Unimate Puma jointed arm robot, the DEA Pragma and Olivetti Sigma Cartesian co-ordinate robots, the Fanuc cylindrical co-ordinate robot, and the Scara jointed arm robot are among those that have been aimed specifically at assembly. The main operations in assembly are to pick something up with a vertical movement, move it horizontally, and then move it down vertically for insertion. These operations need to be performed quickly and smoothly. Therefore, a robot that

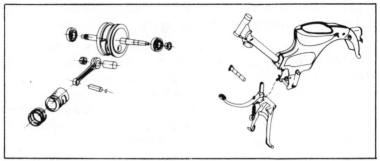

Fig 9.1   Some typical assemblies: The crankshaft assembly, left, can be sub-assembled by robot, but insertion of the connecting rod between the flywheels as the pin is pressed in is handled more easily by hard automation. The assembly on the right needs to be redesigned for robot assembly

can move horizontally and vertically as a basic axis of movement, and which can apply a pressure in these planes seems best for assembly. Also, the robot should be able to cover a fairly large table but should be as small as practicable. Another requirement is some form of compliance – that is self-centering – so that if the pin, for example, is offered to the hole slightly misaligned, it will align itself automatically with the hole. Of course, this compliance can be incorporated in the gripper, but a certain amount can also be incorporated in the robot itself. (Fig. 9.2, 9.3, 9.4)

Pure horizontal and vertical movement are easily provided by the Cartesian and cylindrical co-ordinate machines, as well as by the Scara, but not by the Puma type jointed arm robot. The Scara has shoulder and elbow joints that pivot on vertical axes, the horizontal arm being mounted on a short pillar. Compliance is inherent in this design, since the robot arm is held in position for assembly by the dc servo motors, and the force of misalignment overcomes the braking force of the motors. This type of compliance can be built into a robot of the Puma jointed arm type as well, but the arm would tend to tilt the part as it moved into position, whereas the Scara keeps the part vertical.

But how much compliance is available, and how much is needed? Toyoda Machine Tool, working on a robot assembly project sponsored by the Japanese government, carried out many investigations into the optimum methods of assembly, and permissible tolerances on misalignment. The work was done on a large Cartesian co-ordinate machine. When a spindle was

Fig 9.2   A Unimation Puma robot with compliant wrist doing assembly work with an indexing table

Fig 9.3   Scara robot configuration

Fig 9.4   Scara robot working envelope

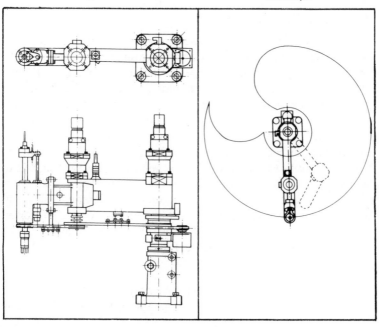

inserted in a housing, it was found that an angular misalignment of up to 1° did not affect the performance. Positional errors of 0.2–0.3mm had little effect on the insertion force, but if the error was 0.4–0.6mm the insertion force increased sharply – but assembly was still possible. Where a press fit was involved, a positional error of 0.4–0.6mm and an angular misalignment of 0.6° were the practical limits. These limits are relatively wide, and suggest that some assembly robots are designed with an unnecessary degree of precision.

A two-speed motor was used to actuate the tool for tightening fasteners, and it drove the fastener down at a speed of 100 rev/min until the torque built up to about 30kg. cm. Then, the tool completed tightening at 2 rev/min. It was found that a positional error of 0.5–0.8mm, and an angular misalignment of 1.5° were permissible. M6, M8 and M10 bolts were used, torques of 125, 300 and 600kg. cm. respectively being applied.

These limits were established without the use of any specially compliant grippers, and demonstrate that for many applications, a specially compliant gripper is unnecessary. However, a number of research groups have developed compliant grippers, notably the Charles Stark Draper Laboratory, Cambridge, Massachusetts, which produced the Remote Centre Compliance (RCC) and IPA, Stuttgart.

The RCC resulted from research into insertion of parts in holes. It was found that to prevent jamming or wedging of the pin in the hole, the gripper needed to be able to articulate the pin about its tip, and to be able to move laterally. The RCC is a sprung device that does just that; thus, for angular misalignment, the pin is articulated so that its tip aligns towards the hole and not away from it. The lateral compliance takes care of misalignment. The RCC was designed for rapid insertion of parts in holes with close tolerances. For example, where a bearing has to be inserted in a hole with a clearance of only 0.01mm, and it was offered to the housing with an angular misalignment of 1° 30 and a lateral misalignment of 1mm, the Laboratory has inserted it in only 0.2s. Clearly, a very powerful aid to the assembly of parts with very small tolerances. (Fig. 9.5)

Case histories

So far though, most robotic assembly has been performed without vision or complex compliant grippers. The DEA

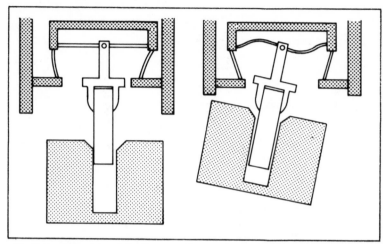

Fig 9.5   Principle of the Remote Centre Compliance device developed
           by the Charles Stark Draper Laboratory

Pragma A 3000 robots, for example, have been used successfully to assemble steering tie rods, diesel injector holders, hydraulic dampers, and pumps. Up to four arms, each with three axes of freedom, plus two optional motions at the wrist, can be installed in one assembly. The control system consists of a DEC LSI 11/2 minicomputer to manage the system, and Intel 8080 based microcomputer controls for each arm, which is guaranteed to be able to place a part within 0.025mm of the nominal position.

To assemble the tie-rod, which consists basically of a housing, washer, two hemispherical cups, and rod with spherical end, two robot arms, each with three axes of movement as well as rotation at the wrist, were adopted. Each is mounted on a slideway beside the workbench. In addition to assembly, the arms grease the ball, load and unload a press, and carry out a functional test when assembly is complete in a cycle of 14s. (Fig. 9.6, 9.7)

The left-hand arm first picks up the inner hemispherical cup and washer, and places them inside the housing. Then, it places the subassembly on the transfer pallet, and greases the joint. Next, the tie-rod is picked up from a pallet which can carry 24 parts, and is inserted in the housing. The pallet then takes the sub-assembly to the work areas of the other arm.

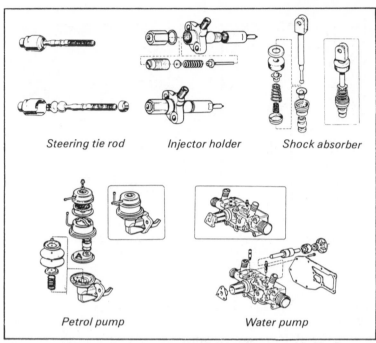

Steering tie rod   Injector holder   Shock absorber

Petrol pump   Water pump

Fig 9.6   Some of the components which can be assembled by Pragma robot

Fig 9.7   Pragma robots assembling tie rods

The right-hand arm has a double gripper, one to pick up the sub-assembly, and the other to unload the finished unit from the press. Therefore, the previous part is removed from the press with one gripper, so that the other gripper can immediately put the new part into the press. This arrangement saves time, of course and can be used in many applications.

Various features are built into the control system. For example, if the washer is not picked up, the arm tries twice more to do so. If it is still unsuccessful, it stops. If there is no cup at the feeder, the robot signals the shortage, and stops. Then, if the arm does not pick up a tie-rod from the expected position in the pallet, it searches through all the positions until one is found.

Whereas the first line was installed to operate with a cycle time of 14s, a line with three arms has been put into use to do the same job at a 10s cycle. The robots are thus comparable to human labour; the more there are, the shorter the cycle time. Unfortunately, however, it is not just a case of adding one robot to the line, as a lot of ancillary equipment is needed. But a robot line can generally be expanded much more quickly and cheaply than a hard automated line.

In another application, valve train components are inserted in different types of engine cylinder head at the rate of 150 an hour. Cylinder heads and sub-assemblies carry magnetic codes, which are read by the robots at each station, and the operations performed include:

☐ Installation of valves and oil seals;
☐ Installation of washers/retainers/springs;
☐ Fitting of upper retainer collars;
☐ Fitting of tappets and screws in the cam block.

For maximum flexibility, each robot station can be a separate island, with parts fed between them by unmanned trolleys. The cylinder heads can go down the line in random order, whereas with conventional automatic assembly machines, one line would be needed for each cylinder head. In many companies, the throughput of perhaps one or two out of five or six designs of cylinder head might warrant automatic assembly. But with the robot line, all the heads can be assembled automatically and at a high rate.

The Scara robot is also being used for a number of assembly

operations. In fact this robot is made by a number of Japanese companies that co-operated in its development. These include Nitto Seiki, Sankyo Seiki, Yamaha Motors NEC, and Pentel. In addition to the two joints in the arm, the wrist can be rotated, the tool can be moved vertically, and in some models, the arm can be moved vertically on the pillar as well. Then, there is the built-in compliance: so long as the object being inserted in a hole strikes the chamfer of the hole, and not the flat surface, it will be inserted successfully. Thus, the axis of the pin needs to be aligned within about 0.5mm of the axis of the hole. In Japan, the Scara robots cost £9,000–12,000 according to size.

Nitto's Picmat-Scara is used mainly for inserting 3–5mm diameter screws, with automatic screw feeders being attached to the tool. In a typical application, in which screws are inserted in door assemblies, a cycle of 3s is needed for each screw. The robot takes 0.5s to move into position, 1s for up and down motion, and 1.5s for screw driving.

Pentel is using its Puha version of the Scara for a very difficult job. The robot inserts a small conical rubber moulding in a mechanical pencil to retain the lead. Since the rubber moulding is very small – approximately 2mm in height – it was decided to pick the moulding directly from the rubber sheet in which it is moulded in an 11 by 11 matrix.

The rubber moulding is inserted at a rotary table, rubber sheets being fed from one side on a conveyor. The metal retaining tip is supplied by a vibratory bowl to the rotary machine, which makes some finishing operations before presenting it to the robot. The robot inserts the rubber in a cycle of 2s.

Yamaha has installed its Came robots on existing assembly lines, often between workers. They are being used in the assembly shops for engines and moped engine/transmission units, where the cycle time is generally 25s. On the moped line, there are 15 robots. The engine crankcase is carried along the line on a pallet, and at the first station the operator places three bearings in recesses in the pallet. Then, the operator loads the crankcase halves on the pallet.

At the next three stations there are three robots; the first two pick up bearings and insert them in the housing, with a light press fit. The third robot lays a bead of sealant around the complex mating face of one crankcase half. The robots on this line generally have three axes of freedom – the two arm joints and vertical motion for the tool – but the robot used to apply sealant can also rotate its wrist to provide an extra axis of movement. The extra axis of motion allows it to apply the sealant more rapidly.

In subsequent operations, robots load and tighten nuts and setscrews. In one case, a washer and nut are both fitted to the end of the crankshaft by an unusual four-axis machine. The washer is fed from a vibratory bowl through a chute to the side of the line, while the nut is loaded on to a pin on the pallet at a previous station. In addition to the normal nutrunning tool, there is an extra open-and-close type gripper hanging vertically from a relay lever pivoting on the tool holder.

This extra gripper picks the washer up from the end of the chute, and drops it over the threaded spindle. The position of the nut on the pallet is such that without moving its arm, the robot can pick up the nut, and spin it down on to the threaded end of the crankshaft. Of course, as the tool descends on to the nut, so the extra gripper is rotated out of the way. A good example of the versatility of the robot. (Fig. 9.8, 9.9, 9.10)

On the line for large engines, there are seven robots in

Fig 9.8   The Yamaha Scara type robot tightening a nut. Attached to the tool is an extra gripper for the washer

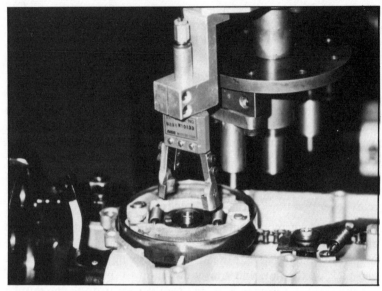

Fig 9.9.   Close-up of the Yamaha gripper shown after dropping the
washer in place

Fig 9.10   Robot installs rubber block between the fins of an engine
cylinder head

crankcase assembly, and eight on final assembly. These are used mainly in place of multiple nutrunners to allow several engines of different sizes to be handled on one line only. At one station, two robots, positioned opposite one another, tighten the eight connecting rod bolts. More robots tighten the setscrews retaining the oil pump strainer, and others the eight screws that retain the sump.

In final assembly, most of the robots do similar work, but at one station, a robot is used to insert rubber anti-vibration blocks between fins in the cylinder head. A vibratory bowl feeder supplies the rectangular rubber blocks, which are approximately 10mm square, to a chute. At the end of the chute, the rubber blocks are fed to a gripper on a short arm. The arm rotates through 180° so that the block is held facing upwards. Then, the robot arm takes the block from the gripper, and moves across to push it down between the fins.

When Yamaha first installed these robots, there were a number of problems. Because the robots were installed on existing manual lines, initially without guards, they were not welcomed by the young women working there. Also, there were failures. At one station, the tools were working very close together; sometimes they would crash, necessitating a repair until the software and controller could be improved.

The robots work with a tolerance of ± 0.2mm, and bowl feeders are used to deliver small parts to the lines. Yamaha plans to automate over 50% of its engine assembly by robot, and usually, one robot is replacing one worker. Since the workers on the line are young, their average pay (1982) was only about £4,000 a year, whereas each robot costs about £10,000, giving a payback period of two and a half years.

Pioneer, the audio company, installed eight Sankyo Skilam robots to insert large square components into printed circuit boards, and it is claimed that the operating efficiency of the line is 99%. NEC is also using two Scara type robots to place five components into a telephone receiver. Parts are delivered by chutes and vibratory bowl feeders.

The attractions of the Scara robot in these applications are its low cost, compact size and compliance. It is expected to have a life of at least five years, whereas hard automation is reckoned to last for two years only on average in Japan. To speed up their payback period, both Pioneer and Pentel operate their machines for 24 hours a day.

Matsushita is also using five simple robots on a tv set assembly line, although virtually all other operations are manual. Each robot is a simple three-axis machine, of the Cartesian co-ordinate type in which the arm is moved vertically on a column, and extends horizontally. In addition, the gripper can move vertically.

At the first station, the robot, fed from a bowl feeder and tube, inserts screws to secure the printed circuit board (pcb) to aluminium brackets. The second robot tightens the screws. At the third station, a robot inserts five connectors, at the fourth, six square transformers, and at the fifth some resistors. In each case, simple chutes, loaded manually with 40–50 parts, are used to supply parts to the robot arm. These chutes are inclined down to the track, the last portion being horizontal of course, and terminating in a stop. The robot arm picks and places the components in turn from the ends of the chutes to the pcb.

All these applications are significant because the robots are simple and inexpensive, and they are installed in existing lines. Thus, the companies are gaining experience at low cost. They are also getting their workers used to the idea of robots, and are proving the ancillary equipment needed for robots. Perhaps that is the most important lesson about robots; it is essential to introduce a few to learn how to get the best out of them.

Cell assembly

Whereas these early Japanese examples were simply cases where robots were used instead of workers or inflexible machines, the robot is better suited to the cell system for assembly, especially where volumes and lot sizes are small. This is where the robot is in a completely different class from hard automation, and its only rival is the human worker.

An interesting example is assembly of dc servo motors by Fanuc in Japan. The company developed the cells in its main factory which until then relied largely on manual assembly. The cell layout depends on the application, of course, but the principle is to use a handling robot – in this case the Fanuc M Model 1 – in the middle of the cell to handle the sub-assembly, and to use assembly robots to do the precise work.

In one case, the cell is arranged alongside a conveyor line, the handling robot transferring a workpiece from the conveyor into the cell, moving the growing sub-assembly around the cell, and the placing the finished assembly back on the conveyor. In this case, the conveyor is moving continuously, a stop holding the incoming workpiece stationary. This cell was designed for less precise assembly, the handling robot inserting some parts which it picked off carousel buffer stores. Then, the final assembly operations were carried out by an assembly robot.

For dc servo motor assembly, there is one Fanuc M Model 1 and three A Model 0 assembly robots in each cell. The main difference between the M and A series is that the M series are designed for bigger loads, while the A series are faster and work to closer tolerances – ±0.05mm against ±0.1mm.

The large M Model 1 robot is in the middle of the cell, with the robot control consoles behind it. At one side of the cell, parallel to the row of consoles is a carousel carrying the rotors, and almost opposite and in line with it, is another carousel for finished assemblies. The three small assembly robots are arranged around the semi-circle with ancillary equipment. Adjacent to the first assembly robot is a small table with a press, and an assembly table with another press built in. The second robot is supplemented by a tie-bolt feeder, while vibratory bowl feeders supply nuts and washers to the third assembly robot. (Fig. 9.11, 9.12)

The operations are ones that suit robot assembly:

☐ An oil seal and bearings are fitted to the rotor;
☐ The rotor is assembled to the flange;
☐ The cover is added;
☐ Tie bolts are inserted;
☐ Nuts and washers are fitted and tightened.

In the first operation, the handling robot transfers the rotor from the carousel to the first assembly table. The assembly robot then places the bearing on the rotor, and the press pushes it down to the shoulder. Then, this operation is repeated for the oil seal, and afterwards, the robot transfers the sub-assembly to a small carousel. However, while the press is in operation, an end cover is transferred to the second assembly table. Then, the robot picks a rotor sub-assembly from the small carousel and

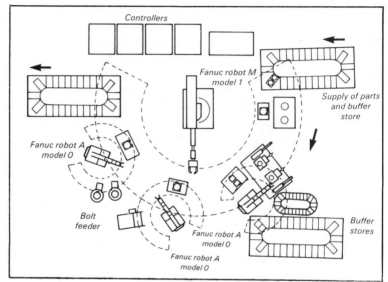

Fig 9.11   A cell designed for the assembly of electric motors

fits it to the end cover. The press incorporated in the table then assembles the rotor to the end cover.

Because the stator is large and heavy, it is lowered over the rotor and on to the end cover by the handling robot. When this operation is complete, the handling robot transfers the assembly to the next station. There, the tie-bolts are loaded into wide

Fig 9.12   Arrangement of the cell for electric motor assembly

chutes so that they arrive at the bottom laid horizontally. To orientate the tie-bolts to suit the robot, a special handling device is used. It grasps the tie-bolt, pulls it away from the chute, and then rotates through 90° so the bolt is vertical. The robot then moves across and picks the tie-bolt from the gripper, and inserts it through the stator. It repeats this operation four times before the handling robot transfers the assembly to the next station.

At the final station, a robot picks and places four washers over the tie-bolts, and then in sequence, spins down and tightens the four nuts. The completed assembly is then transferred by the handling robot to the carousel for finished motors.

Although this seems a complex arrangement, with the presses and special equipment, all the equipment is under the control of one system, while the presses, for example, are cheap and simple units similar to those found in thousands of factories. Then, Fanuc operates the cell continuously to produce 300 motors in the 24 hour shift; with manual operation, each man was producing 30 motors in an eight-hour shift. It is claimed that assembly costs are reduced by 30%. In fact, to further operation, Fanuc adopted a linear organisation for robot assembly of servo

Fig 9.13   A cell built around one Unimation Puma robot for the assembly of electric motors at the National Engineering Laboratory, Scotland

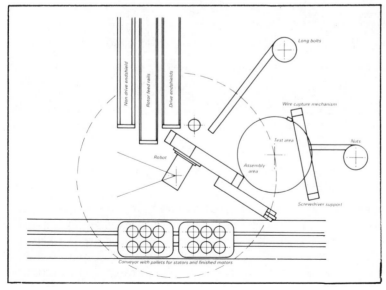

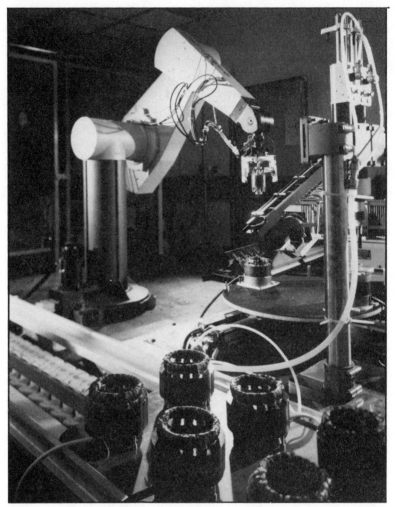

Fig 9.14   Using a special gripper the Puma at NEL inserts the rotor into the stator

motors in its new factory. This was designed to produce 10,000 units monthly.

But is it as flexible as robot assembly is supposed to be? Its flexibility lies in the fact that as output increases, so capacity can be increased gradually. These days, companies are not keen to take on extra staff for every small increase of output, and it is not practicable to make regular small increases in the output of hard automation. Also, so long as the weights of the assemblies do not differ too much, the cell can be used to assemble different motors. With common bolt sizes, different motors could, in theory, be assembled in random order but this would impose quite a burden on the staff supplying parts to the cells.

Fanuc prefers to leave the delivery of parts to the cells to men, not least because the presence of men in the shop is a good control on quality – and it gives flexibility. These case studies demonstrate that existing robots, with ancillary equipment, are suitable for many assembly operations now. The systems are not completely flexible, nor fully developed, but they demonstrate that now is the time to use robots in assembly. (Fig. 9.13, 9.14)

CHAPTER TEN

Future sensing for assembly –
and other jobs

WHAT is the answer to giving the robot complete flexibility? Some believe the answer lies in a complex system with different tools and grippers, while others put their faith in vision. Tactile sensing is also seen as the solution, as are robots and devices that can learn as they assemble parts to do the job more precisely, by learning from the previous batch. With currently available control systems, it is possible to devise a machine that bends a blade or screws a cap down to obtain a certain clearance, and which takes the adjustments made in the last 30 or so operations into account in making the next adjustment. Indeed, since such techniques are already in use in factories, they are likely to form part of any robotic assembly system before long.

One attempt to build a completely flexible system with existing levels of technology was made in Japan under government sponsorship – in fact, it was just part of a flexible manufacturing project. It was designed to assemble large gearboxes and bearing housings weighing up to about 30kg.

The robot assembly system was built by Toyoda Machine Tool. It consists of three robots:

☐ One to mount the parts on a pallet;
☐ One for assembly;
☐ and one for bolt/nut tightening.

At the first station, an arm of the polar type is mounted alongside a fixture that can carry two pallets. This is a four-axis robot, and adjacent is a tool drum carrying six grippers. The robot arm loads the workpieces on the pallet in various positions. (Fig. 10.1)

At the second station, there are two arms mounted on a

Fig 10.1   Massive assembly robot built as part of an experimental
flexible manufacturing system in Japan

massive four-post structure approximately 4m × 2m by 3m
high. Both arms are of the Cartesian type, and each has four
axes of freedom. In addition, the pallet carrier can rotate to give
a ninth degree of freedom. On one side of the structure are a pair
of horizontal rails along which the arm and its carrier can slide.
The telescopic arm can also move vertically. The overhead arm
hangs down from a beam so that it, too, can move in the x and y
and z axes. The wrists of both arms can be rotated.

Adjacent to the arms, but outside the table, are circular drum-
type tool carriers. These have vertical axes, and the one near the
horizontal arm carries grippers of many types – including one
with remote compliance – while the other carries a variety of
tools. There is a separate small fixture with a gantry-mounted
Cartesian arm which is to be used to tighten screws and nuts.

The system was designed to assemble gearboxes and spindle/
bearing/housing assemblies weighing up to 30kg. In the sample
gearbox, there are two parallel shafts, each carrying a gear,
while the housing consists of a central portion with end plates.
The sample spindle housing contained a stepped spindle carried
on a number of bearings of different types.

The principle of operation of the assembly system is that a

trolley, following cables in the floor, takes components to the mounting robot, and then carries them on to the main assembly robot and fastening robot. Subsequently, the assembly would pass to an automatic inspection machine. There is a tower carrying about 20 pallets and assemblies serving as a buffer store, and the trolley can take the assemblies to and from the store to the various robots to allow assembly in random order.

Clearly, this is a very elaborate system, designed to allow almost unmanned assembly. But as the project has progressed, so ideas on flexible manufacture have changed. Now, the system seems too universal and large to be practical, although the principle is feasible – at a price.

Vision and sensory gripping

Many companies have demonstrated robots with visual sensing, and some are in use, but as yet the cameras are too expensive and not suitable for most factory environments. Currently, a vision system – camera and processors – costs about £15,000, and until the price can be cut to one-third of this, applications will remain very limited. Probably by 1985 research and manufacture will have produced some realistic systems at realistic prices. In the meantime, various systems have been developed, and some prototypes are in use.

For example, the Production Engineering Research Association (PERA) in the UK has developed a simple system to orientate and check parts optically. It consists of a vibratory bowl feeder, camera and imaging device, and the INA pick-and-place robot. Two thin lines of optical fibres are embedded in the track, and they transfer a single-line plan and elevation view of the component to a linescan camera. Since the components are pushed past the optical fibres at constant speed, a two-dimensional silhouette is built up from successive scans. This system checks the orientation of the part, and can also reject incorrectly supplied parts. It is a coarse system, able to differentiate between parts where their size is at least 5% different. Therefore, it cannot distinguish between parts that are within and just outside machined tolerances. But the system is on the way to such differentiation, and has the merit of being simple and relatively inexpensive.

One of the most comprehensive robotic vision was Westinghouse's APAS – adaptable programmable assembly

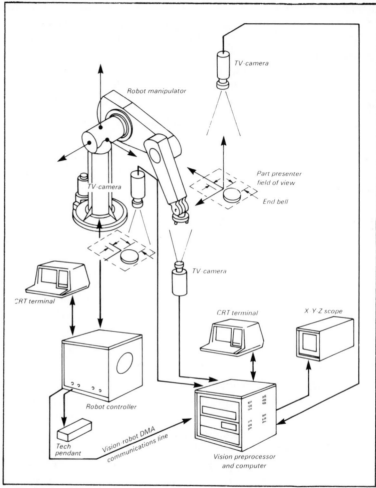

Fig 10.2   Westinghouse APAS project involves the use of robots and vision system

system – which was funded partly by the US government. The aim was to build a flexible assembly line with vision for the production of 450 different styles of electric motor. Batch sizes were to be about 600, with 13 batches a day. The project was started in 1976, and ended in 1982. (Fig. 10.2)

The assembly lines were built as closed loops, with power-free buffered conveyors about 10m long. There were five single and one double assembly stations per loop, designed to work to a

15s cycle. The vision system inspects the part for assembly, and determines its exact location and orientation so that the robot can pick it up and perform the next assembly operation. The vision system consists of:

☐ 128 × 128 pixel solid state cameras;
☐ Vision preprocessor and vision processing module;
☐ An oscilloscope to display x-y-z data;
☐ Tektronix graphics display terminal;
☐ Robot and controller.

The robot controller interacts with the vision module through a direct memory access (dma) communications line.

The cycle time for the most complicated task was 7.5s, while the vision system needed 1.5s to process its data. Although the researchers claim they have demonstrated the feasibility of assembly with vision, they do not consider the hardware suitable yet – but think it soon will be. This view was echoed by Kristian Aareskjold, robot divisional manager, Trallfa, who said: 'Even if vision and other sensings techniques were available now (1982) they would not lead to massive increases in the sales of robots. The problem is that these sensors are restrictive and inflexible.'

But what are the applications for vision in assembly? Work at General Motors in the USA has shown that the best use is to check whether parts are present after an assembly operation – systems are in use to do this on valve collets on engine cylinder heads – and to check the orientation of a part for a robot to pick it up. General Motors' Consight system is based on structured light, which allows the sensor to detect the geometry of the part directly. Automatix, which has designed a Cartesian co-ordinate robot with associated vision system for assembly, envisages similar applications. (Fig. 10.3)

However, Fiat has experimented with vision to pick up parts positioned randomly in a pallet and to assemble and inspect them with vision. What's more, this equipment has been installed in the Rivalta car factory in northern Italy. The system consists of a Fairchild camera with 488 × 380 pixels, a minicomputer controller, and an ASEA robot. The system was used to attach door hinges to doors, and in that application, the camera gave a field of vision 500 × 400mm, and a resolution of about 1mm². The door is carried on a conveyor so that the holes for the hinge bolts are within 2cm of their correct position. The position of the

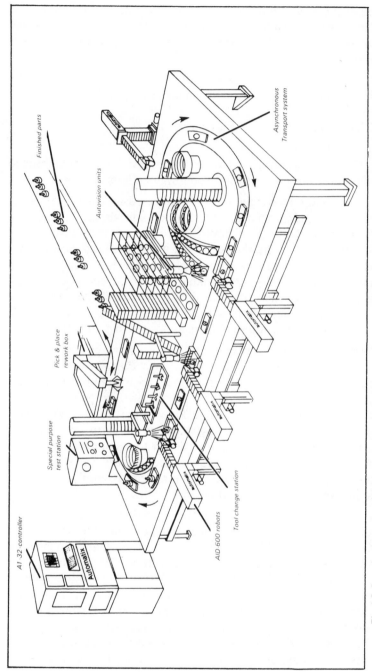

Finished parts

Autovision units

Asynchronous
Transport system

Pick & place
rework box

Special purpose
test station

A1-32 controller

AID 600 robots

Tool change station

Fig 10.3   Automatix multi-arm assembly system using an asynchronous transport system and vision stations

holes is seen and calculated in 5s, while the robot picks up the hinge. The hinge is inserted, and the bolts are tightened in 12s by the robot which uses multiple drivers. Fiat claims that over a period of about three months, the robot system was used to attach hinges to 10,000 doors of Fiat Ritmo cars with only 224 failures. The system can handle four different doors. (Fig. 10.4)

Fig 10.4   Fiat has used a robot with visual sensing to attach hinges to car doors. The control system was developed for multiple visual sensing. Top: the automated hinge bolting station. Bottom: configuration of the industrial vision system. The operation has two stages: move door and calculate the position of the holes (5s); hinge clamped by robot to door (12s)

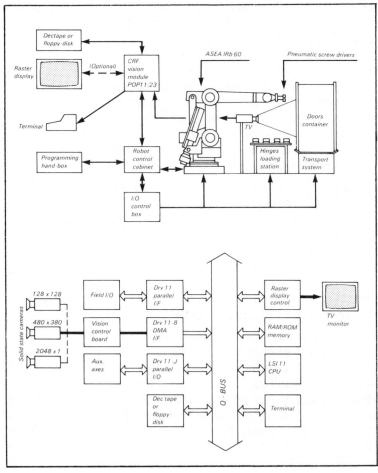

In assembly, the problem with vision is that it is very difficult to use visual sensing in the way a human sees things. The existing systems are only two-dimensional – but with more than one camera, distance can be calculated – and they cannot cope with big differences in intensity of light. If it were desirable to set up a station with one robot and vision sensing to take care of a number of jobs, a very complex and expensive system would result.

For example, it would be possible for one camera to show a number of grippers, so that the robot could select the correct one for each job. Another camera could indicate what parts are coming, and another the bins of parts available. But unless the parts are stacked so that they do not touch, current systems cannot distinguish between them. And what about assembly itself? To guide a part into a housing, the vision system would need to respond very quickly to what the camera shows. Also, the cameras would need to be able to locate the position of the tool and housing with great precision in a dynamic situation. The simple fact is that vision systems are not precise enough, but robots are. Therefore, although robots with vision systems may seem very exciting, at present they do not seem to meet the needs of real industrial life as far as assembly is concerned – except where assembly and inspection are combined.

But there is certainly a need for better tactile sensing or for robots that learn. Hitachi's learning robot with 'sensory table' is one example. It consists of a six-axis Cartesian coordinate robot for coarse motion, and a table for fine motion. It is intended for assembly of parts with close tolerances, such as bearings in housings, and is designed to 'learn' to assemble correctly. The robot is a pick-and-place device, which would first transfer a housing from a parts feeder to the table, and then pick up a bearing or spindle and insert it in the housing. (Fig. 10.5)

In the table is a frame of stainless steel beams, each carrying a semiconductor strain gauge. The beams are arranged so that the strain gauges detect lateral force, in the x and y planes, and tilting forces resulting from the assembly operation. Therefore when a component is inserted, the sensory table measures the forces, and the controller calculates whether the table needs to be tilted or moved laterally to improve alignment. The table is then moved accordingly a step at a time, after each insertion, the

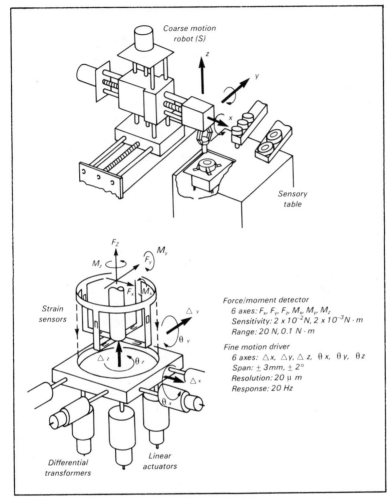

Fig 10.5   Hitachi's experimental learning system consists of a simple robot with multi-directional force sensor on the table

first change in position usually making the biggest reduction in insertion time. It is claimed that with a clearance of 20 microns, the time needed for insertion is reduced from about 10 to 6s after one operation, and to 3–4s after 20–30.

There is one 16–bit processor to look after sensor processing, another for servo processing, and an 8–bit processor to control communications. Of course, this is a very complex device with its strain gauges and microprocessors, and it is doubtful whether it will be able to survive a factory environment. Indeed, the compliant gripper seems a more satisfactory approach. Hitachi has also designed some jointed arm robots with visual sensing for assembly work. The interesting feature of these is that they have two microprocessors, one to control the robot's normal functions, and the other to control external sensors, such as vision. As electronic parts reduce in price, the use of many processors will become commonplace. (Fig. 10.6, 10.7)

In assembly, the gripper is a key component. Since the robot is an expert at picking things up, the trend is to use many grippers, and for the robot to select the one it needs for the job. These can be simple grippers designed for parts of different sizes, some tools such as screwdrivers, compliant grippers, and even grippers with soft touch and some special sensing features. Of course not all are needed at one station.

The alternative of a universal gripper, resembling a human hand, is attractive to researchers but is not really needed in the factory. Different types of sensors are needed, but it is more practical to use simple grippers than a universal one. For example, a gripper with the capability of twᴜ fingers and a thumb of the human hand would have about 15 degrees of freedom and tactile sensors; a very complex device.

What is needed in many applications is a gripper that can grip parts with the corrrect amount of pressure, and identify the part it is holding. One solution, in research terms, is the gripper developed by Hull University. Pressure sensitive elements are

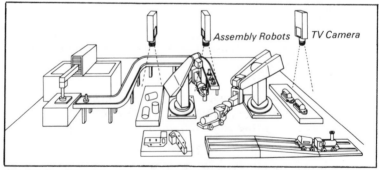

Fig 10.6   Hitachi's view of future robot assembly with vision. The sensory table fits bearings to spindles, while the other robots carry out remaining assembly tasks

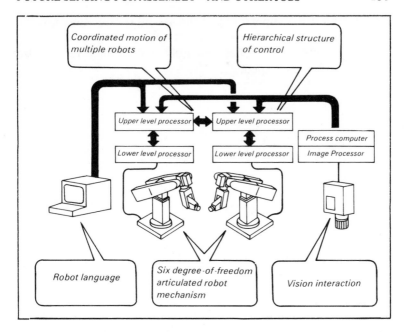

Fig 10.7   Interfaces and information paths in the Hitachi vision system

arranged in a four by four matrix in the palms of the gripper, one of which also carries an array of spaced out optical fibres. In the palm opposite is a light source. Thus, the pressure sensitive pads can be used to indicate the pressure applied, and with a feedback system, the pressure can be regulated accordingly. The optical system, based on photo diodes, can check that the part being gripped is of the expected shape, and when it is in the correct position for gripping.

Many researchers are investigating different approaches to the problem of gripping, with multi-finger designs, grippers incorporating rollers to detect slippage and so on. Most require complex electronic controllers, which is further evidence of how dependent on electronics robot systems are. This trend will accelerate, of course, but it will not alter the fact that in a factory, the simplest solution is usually the best. Currently, simple robots are in use in assembly lines and cells, and similar units can be used in many more applications. With time, the precision and sensitivity of robots will increase, so that they can work with less specialised ancillary equipment. But the fundamental techniques are unlikely to change in the foreseeable future, even if the appearance of the assembly shop may change dramatically. What is important is that the advantages and challenges offered by robot assembly, particularly in medium volume work are grasped.

CHAPTER ELEVEN

The multitude of miscellaneous jobs

WHAT sets the robot apart from other forms of automation is the vast number of jobs it can do. And what makes it so difficult for the production engineer and factory manager is that many are uneconomic. For example, a robot could be used to remove pressings from a small press and palletise them; but it makes much more sense to use a small pusher, a chute, and a strategically placed pallet. That is a clear-cut case, but there will be many where fashion suggests a robot, but where there is a simpler and more effective solution. The robot is no cure-all.

Nevertheless, a number of jobs that may not seem appropriate at first sight are proving economic. There are other jobs that must be automated because poor working conditions are leading to poor quality and a high labour turnover, which costs the company money – even though much of the cost may be borne by the personnel department. In many of these jobs, the robot is the answer.

Among the straightforward jobs for robots are laying beads of sealant or adhesive, drilling, and inspection, which could well turn out to be one of the biggest 'miscellaneous' uses. Other important jobs are deburring, fettling of castings and leak testing.

'Fixed in place' (FIP) gaskets, which consist of a bead of sealant laid on the mating faces, have come into use to cut manufactured costs and improve quality. A number of robotic devices are available to lay these beads of sealant, and of course they can lay a bead of constant section very accurately. They are usually sold in conjunction with the sealant delivery system, so that they may appear expensive, but they are cost-effective owing to the speed with which they can apply the bead, and the reduced waste. For normal surfaces, a three-axis machine is adequate, usually of the Cartesian co-ordinate type, but if the surface is not flat, some articulation at the wrist is useful. For example, Yamaha Motors used a simple three-axis machine to apply sealant to an engine crankcase housing in about 15s. (Fig. 11.1)

The application of adhesive is similar to that of sealant, and there are many uses in the automotive and electrical industries now, but these will increase as companies use more bonded structures to reduce weight and costs. A typical use is to apply adhesive to the bonnets and bootlids of a car. British Leyland is using a Unimate Puma robot to apply 63 spots of adhesive to the stiffener for the bootlid on the Triumph Acclaim, and an ASEA robot to apply beads of adhesive to the tailgate of the Mini Metro hatchback.

Fig 11.1   A three-axis robot laying a bead of sealant on a crankcase half

The 63 spots are applied to the Acclaim bootlid stiffener in 58s, which is twice as fast as a man could do the job. The company claims that the robot can operate for 98% of the working day, which is 16 hours. In practice, the operators would have been likely to achieve about 14 hours a day, so with automated loading, not used in this case, the increase in productivity is substantial – and of course, laying adhesive is a dirty job. In the Mini Metro plant, the ASEA robot is applying one 4.3m bead and three beads each 100m long on the tailgate outer panel in 20s.

A more recent application can be found at Dagenham, UK, at the Ford plant (Fig 11.2) where two ASEA robots apply sealer to the wheelarches.

Another unexpected application is the laying up of wiring harnesses for forklift trucks and any other large assembly. Lansing Bagnall developed a Unimate Puma, suspended overhead, for this job, because there were so many variations in the electrical equipment on its different models. The job was done manually, but with the large number of variations involved, there were frequent problems as operators worked out which ones had to be done. Once the systems had been developed, the robot proved very quick and consistent.

Deburring is another job with a lot of potential, and already some ASEA robots are being used for this job. Ford of Europe

Fig 11.2   A single ASEA IRb6 robot per line applies sealer to the wheelarches of the Ford Sierra body in white at Dagenham, UK.

has installed two deburring robots in a plant in the UK, and two more in Germany. They are used to deburr forged steel wheel spindles and cast iron steering knuckles. One robot operates in conjunction with a rotary table and carries a high-speed motor that rotates a carbide tool at 18,000 rev/min. It deburrs the components in pairs, the operator loading/unloading while the robot is working. Of course, the robot is enclosed, the operator loading outside the cell. At the end of the cycle, the table rotates, and the workpieces and jigs pass through windows in the cell wall. This is an application that may not seem too attractive to managers, owing to the need for the enclosure, but it makes a big difference both to the noise level in the shop, and to the working conditions of the operator. (Fig. 11.3)

If deburring is a monotonous and noisy job, then the fettling

Fig 11.3   An ASEA IRb6 being used to deburr a steering knuckle

of iron castings is an almost intolerable one. The operator has to wear much protective clothing and wields a heavy grinder or implement. In some foundries, the men just stand above the line and wield sledge hammers to knock off the runners and risers. Usually, it is too hot for protective clothing to be worn, so it is not surprising that turnover in such jobs is usually more than 100% a year. But even where the fettling operation involves grinding with a dust extractor, it is a tiring and dirty job. The robot offers the potential of eliminating these jobs, and of improving productivity and quality – wherever working conditions are bad, the robot must make improvements in both. Each operator fettles a variety of parts without any jigging, and despite the roughness of the job, skill is needed to grind the flash off smoothly without digging into the casting. Of course, occasionally the operator does dig in, and the result is scrap.

Existing robots are used to fettle some large castings, but for small workpieces, some precision is needed. To solve this problem, IPA, Stuttgart has devised a cell concept in which a robot uses a tool that senses the condition of the casting. The robot is installed in a noise proofed room, and fettles workpieces mounted on an indexing table. In addition, the robot can pick up the casting and hold it against a belt grinder. The key development in this cell is a sensor/tool holder that can follow profiles and measure their difference from a predetermined form. The sensor/tool holder is designed so that it can pivot about the centre of gravity of the grinding wheel. (Fig. 11.4)

*Fig 11.4   A combined tool/sensor devised to measure
contours and hold the tool for fettling*

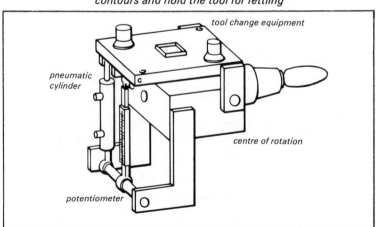

First, the robot is taught the correct finished profiles of the castings it will handle. These data indicate both the height and width of the flash, since both factors affect the pressure that must be applied to grind the casting to the correct profile. Then, when the casting is mounted on the table, the robot moves the grinding wheel across the unfettled surface without grinding. Since the grinding wheel is displaced by the flash, the profile is measured. The data are then transferred to the controller which calculates the pressure that should be applied, and the fettling operation takes place. To compensate for tool wear, the cutter is moved up to a datum point before each fettling operation, and allowances made as necessary. This is an elegant solution to a difficult problem, and one that almost certainly has other applications. (Fig. 11.5)

In the aerospace industry, there is a demand for a method of drilling a big variety of stiffeners and panels with great precision. These panels are usually curved, so a conventional drilling approach is a lengthy business. Then, when aircraft undergo major refitting, many panels are removed by drilling through the rivets. Although the requirement for such precision may be peculiar to the aerospace industry there are many other products where rapid, programmable drilling has a place.

British Aerospace is already using a Cincinnati Milacron T3 to drill a number of holes in aircraft skin panels. These panels

Fig 11.5   Comparison betwen the burr on a casting and the ideal shape, together with the signals received during processing and the contact pressure during fettling

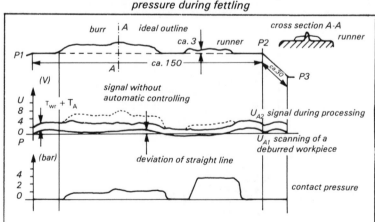

are curved, and there are a large number of variations. The robot is equipped with a compliant drilling head produced by Taylor Hitec. The head drills and countersinks the panel, and then inserts clips, indexing from one operation to another. The robot aligns the head approximately, and the head then takes up any misalignment with the drill bushes – the compliant head can compensate for up to 0.6mm, with a feed start position error of 1mm. Since the panels need to be interchangeable, the holes must be placed within 0.025mm of the nominal position. This is a rather specialised industry, but there are many other companies where a drilling robot would be useful, especially if it can be taught the program simply by being led through it. (Fig. 11.6)

Inspection is likely to be dominated by robots in the near future, but one application that demonstrates the ability of the robot to turn up in unexpected places is leak testing of cars. For an accurate measure of leaks, helium gas is being used in several plants instead of air-under-water tests, but the car is a difficult job to handle. Therefore, the normal method is to pass the car

Fig 11.6   Drilling by robot with a compliant head fitted

through a tunnel in which water is sprayed at it through jets. Leak detection depends on the ability and conscientiousness of the operator, which cannot be guaranteed. Moreover, if a window is left open, or the car does leak badly, a lot of damage is done; it is not so much the materials cost as the cost of rectification that is the problem.

To overcome this problem BL is using a pair of Trallfa robots to detect leaks of helium from some of its cars. A trace of helium, is injected into the car body at low pressure, and the robots, equipped with delicate sensors, detect any leaks. The painted and trimmed body with vents taped over, is lowered on to a jig for precise location and then moves on a conveyor through the robot station. Not unexpectedly, the body has to be located very accurately through the station, and a tolerance of ± 1.5mm is needed. The helium is injected, and after making a sweep over the windscreen area, the robots move the sensors to calibration points at adaptors in the open apertures for the door mirrors. If the level is correct – if not there is a major leak at a vent – the robots move the sensors across the critical areas of the body, always within 25mm of the metal surface. The robot can move the sensor at up to 300mm/s, and traverses successfully, despite the fact that the body is moving along the track. The system was designed for a cycle of 1min 52s. (Fig. 11.7)

Of course, this system measures leakage with great accuracy,

Fig 11.7   A pair of Trallfa robots being used at British Leyland test car bodies for leaks

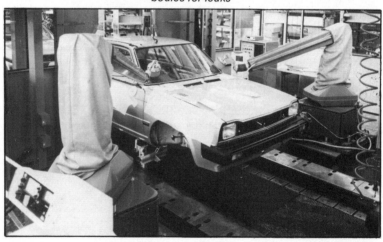

and provides data on trends in leakage as well as serious problems. Thus, management has the opportunity of rectifying a problem before it becomes serious. Clearly, an excellent application, and one that can save a lot of money in rectification costs. Apart from the elimination of damage, the fact that the car is without wheels, power train, seats and carpets, means the rectification can be done much more quickly and cheaply than before. Another case of an unexpected bonus coming from the use of a robot.

The aim of inspection in a modern plant is not so much to reject defective parts, as to prevent them being made. It is sometimes said half seriously that more productive machines allow scrap to be produced more quickly, but certainly, the faster a machine is turning out parts, the faster the operator needs to know the trend in tolerances. Robotic systems are needed to give the necessary flexibility, and the measuring system needs to be connected to a computer so that the results can be interpreted and changes to tools made in time to prevent scrap being produced. Current gauging equipment is limited to a small range of parts, while the co-ordinate measuring machines used in metrology laboratories are too slow. What is needed is a system combining the speed of operation of a robot with the equipment of a co-ordinate measuring machine.

In Italy, DEA has devised just such a system, combining the principles of its measuring machines and the Pragma Cartesian co-ordinate robot. A horizontal measuring arm, with three or four axes of freedom, serves as the carrier for the measuring probe. In view of the need for precision, it is carried on air bearings, and has high-resolution non-contact linear position measuring devices. It is equipped with a number of attachments, such as probes and sensors. Since the arm can move at up to 500m/s, and can measure at 80mm/s, the machine can inspect critical dimensions on all parts produced. One, two or four arms can be incorporated in one system, to cope with great variety in high volume. (Fig. 11.8)

The machine inspects at two levels. First, it carries out the dimensional checks on the part, indicates whether that is acceptable or not, and diverts rejects from the line. Then, a minicomputer carries out a statistical analysis, and the results can be fed to the controllers of the various machines to prevent tolerances drifting too far. This is the feature that can make the

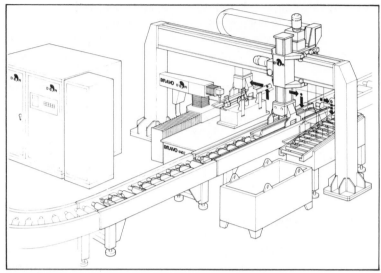

Fig 11.8   A DEA automatic assembly station for tractor shoes

system pay for itself in a highly automated plant.

So far, machines have been installed to check aluminium cylinder heads and shoes for tracked vehicles. Previously, the cylinder heads were inspected on a conventional co-ordinate measuring machine, which took 40 minutes for each component, allowing only 24 components, or 7% of output to be checked on one machine daily. With the new machine, 165 points can be measured in 2min 48s, so that 320 components are measured in eight-hour shifts. The machine that handles tractor shoes is integrated into a conveyor system, a gantry-mounted handling robot transferring the component between the conveyor and fixture. The shoe is clamped in position automatically. There are 70 different shoes, and 11 dimensions are checked, while the machine also makes two calculations of squareness and two of flatness from the measured data. All this is done in a cycle of 58s, so that 840 shoes can be checked daily on two shifts.

This is a highly specialised machine, but one that offers great flexibility in inspection. It is also an important concept in unmanned manufacture, where components are manufactured and measured automatically, the drift from tolerance being caught, in theory, before any defective parts can be produced. It will take some time before such plants become a reality, but the elements are now emerging.

CHAPTER TWELVE
Robot trolleys

THERE does not seem to be much robotic about unmanned trolleys, except the slightly uncanny way in which they glide noiselessly across the workshop floor. They seem to be little more than ancillary equipment, but they are the flexible alternative to the conveyor, and have a place in robotic applications.

Without these unmanned trolleys, conveyors are one of the automated factory's necessary evils. They are evil in that they wear out, break down too often, and they are noisy. They are also symbolic of what is hated about automation by many workers. It is the conveyor, clanking remorselessly on all day, that makes the worker feel a prisoner of the machine, forced to work at an unnatural pace. Of course, managers see it in a different light; in many cases, they feel that owing to union pressure they are unable to run the line as fast as they would like. Therefore, the elimination of the conveyor brings benefit all round. Again, it is the smaller company that stands to gain as much as anyone from unmanned trolleys; conveyors are usually too inflexible for him.

Of course, the term 'robot trolley' is used to cover all sorts of devices, from a trolley that can just travel between two or three places, following cables buried in the floor, to a computer-controlled device that can follow many different paths, and load and unload itself. Trolleys with built in robot arms are not used, and at present, the robot arm seems more effective if standing somewhere else. But that situation may change. In flexible systems, the use of a trolley with a robot arm and locations for tools can eliminate the need for manned intervention at the machine tool.

One of the most commonly used robot trolleys is the Robotrailer made by Digitron in Switzerland, and Murata in

Japan. It can turn through corners with fairly tight radii, and a lift is incorporated for self-loading and unloading. Both Volvo and Fiat use these, and indeed, most of the new flexible systems devised by Fiat's production engineering company, Comau, seem to involve the use of robot trolleys.

One of the earliest applications was in the area where the power trains and suspensions are mounted in the body. Fiat decided to automate the mounting operation on its 131 Mirafiori car, and so needed to assemble the suspension, steering, engine transmission and rear axle on a fixture prior to this operation. It was decided to build these sub-assemblies up on the fixtures while they were sitting on robot trolleys. Men work at several work stations, with bins of parts behind them. The engines and transmissions come across on overhead conveyors and are lowered on to the trolleys, and then the men build up the various units on the fixtures. Since there is no assembly line, they work at their own speed, and when they have finished, the trolley moves off to a marshalling area before going to the powertrain/body mounting area. There, the fixture is lifted clear of the trolley, which recirculates, and is subsequently used to hold the mechanical units in the correct position as they are offered up to the body. (Fig. 12.1)

Then, of course, the Fiat Robogate system uses robot trolleys to transfer bodies between the Robogates, thus increasing the flexibility of the system, albeit at a cost in terms of space. Sofim also uses robot trolleys to transfer diesel engines between final assembly and test and despatch, this particular plant producing a family of engines.

More recently, Fiat has introduced its Lavorazione Asincrone Motore (LAM) engine assembly system, in which robot trolleys play an important part. The idea of this system is to automate as much of assembly as possible, but to keep it flexible. Therefore, hard automation, in the form of four automatic assembly transfer lines, is used to do the jobs that can be easily automated, and which are common to variations in a family of engines. There are 175 workers/shift in the plant, and they work at 10 assembly islands, each of which has 12 work stations. The islands and transfer lines are fed by 37 trolleys, each carrying a pair of engines between stations. Unlike the Robogate, though, the trolley unloads its engines at the islands, and then moves on to transfer some more units. The complete system is under

Fig 12.1   Robot trolleys are used by Fiat as work stations for chassis
assembly, and to transfer the assemblies to the body mounting area

computer control, not just to deliver the engines in the optimum
sequence, but also to store data on what has been produced, and
where there are hold ups.

An important feature of this system is that the men work
remotely from the high-speed transfer lines, such a layout being
practical only with trolleys. Whereas Fiat uses these trolleys
instead of a conveyor line, thus giving the workers more
freedom, unmanned trolleys can also be used when it is needed

Fig 12.2   Trolley on rails loads buffer stores and automatic pallet
changers in the Yamazaki flexible machining system

to improve the handling at an existing plant but there is no space
for a conveyor system; the trolleys can use existing gangways,
and of course, they can often be used to replace fork lift trucks.

In Japan, Fanuc, Murata, and Yamazaki, have all used the
concept of the robot trolley to develop unmanned machining
systems based on NC machines. In the Murata and Fanuc
systems, the trolleys move between automated warehouses and
work stations, a pusher loading the pallet on to the trolley. In the
Fanuc system, the trolley delivers the pallet to buffer stores,
moving between a pair of rails with the platform carrying the
workpiece in the raised position. The trolley stops, and lowers
the platform, leaving the pallet on the rails. In the Murata plant,
the trolley has its own slide mechanism, and so when it reaches
the machine tool, it pushes the pallet straight on to the vacant
pallet changer. In the Yamazaki system, the trolley runs on rails
alongside the machine tools, and transfers the pallet between
loading station and buffer stores, and between buffer stores and
pallet changer. (Fig. 12.2). Recently Yamasaki, Hitachi Seiki
and several other Japanese machine tool companies have
adopted trolleys following cables in the floor as essential features
of FM5.

These trolleys are controlled to follow a certain route at a

Fig 12.3   Two Robotrailers are used to transfer workpieces and pallets
between seven machining centres and a warehouse

certain time, and to load and unload as necessary. In fact, in the
Murata system, a minicomputer controls the machining centres,
pallet changers, trolleys and the automatic warehouse. They are
not necessarily expensive; Murata uses two Robotrailers to
supply seven machines, and they can operate with up to 10
machining centres; of course, this depends to some extent on the
cycle times, which are 20–40min at Murata (Fig. 12.3)

Current robot trolleys offer a means of cutting manning levels
in handling, in asssembly, machining and welding operations, so
long as pallets are used to carry the workpieces. Of course, since
they have to follow cables in the floor, they are not completely
flexible. In addition, their handling systems are limited, but like
fully-fledged robots, they can be controlled by a central
computer for optimum operation. (Fig. 12.4)

Trolleys that can be programmed to follow any route are
under development, and these obviously have advantages over
the current machines. In the long term, the maintenance of the
cable guidance system could increase the attractiveness of a
truly robotic trolley. These are self-steering, and are taught by
the operator as he drives along, operating a teach box through a
joystick. In one design, the trolley senses its position with the aid

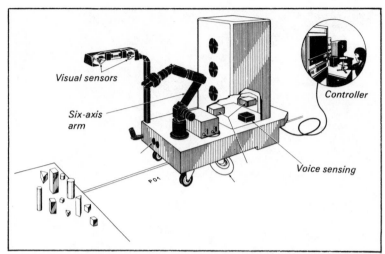

Fig 12.4   A prototype trolley/robot fitted with two visual sensors to
guide the arm. Others detect obstructions and read station numbers.
There are sensors also for voice synthesis and object recognition

of a two-axis gyro and optical encoders, which count the revolu-
tions of the wheels. Ultrasonic sensors detect obstacles. At the
loading stations, optical sensors help berth the trolley
accurately. Roller conveyors on the trolley, and at the loading
stations are used for loading/unloading.

This system seems adequate in theory, but the fact that the
trolley is measuring its movement and angle only can lead to
errors. For example, the tyres can wear, the gyro can drift and if
the trolley passed over a patch of oil, the wheels could slip. If the
slippage occurred on a corner, the trolley could straighten up
too early, and go well off course. It is true that any obstacle
would be sensed, but frequent errors would play havoc with
delivery schedules; after all, the object of the device is to operate
with the regularity of a conveyor, but with more flexibility.
Therefore, some method by which the trolley can find its
position against some known datum line seems essential in a
factory. Presumably, the ultrasonic sensors could be used for
this, but all these things add to the cost.

In certain applications, such as in nuclear power stations, a
combined trolley and handling robot is a necessity. But in the
factory environment, where space for gangways is limited, the
cable guidance system is probably more cost-effective. (Fig.
12.5)

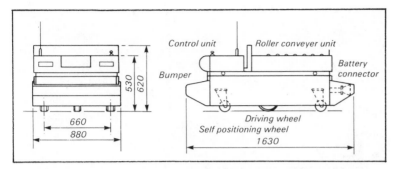

Fig 12.5   A prototype robot trolley with its own guidance system

There is also potential for a trolley combined with a pick-and-place device. For example, in many workshops, a large automated warehouse is an unnecessary expense. Where parts are stocked in bins, and are not picked at too great a frequency, it might be economic to have trolley/arms moving around in the

Fig 12.6   Two of the basic elements of any FMS installation – the trolley and the pallet changer

Fig 12.7   An FMS for machining machine tool parts

stores, picking parts, and then transferring them to the worksta-
tions. To do their job efficiently, these would need some form of
vision sensing. The whole procedure would be under computer
control, so precise stock levels in the stores and at the line would
be known. The concept of a robot on wheels that can do any job
is appealing, and it is likely to have a place in the service
industries, and eventually in machine maintenance, but in most
plants, it looks as if the use of improved versions of unguided
trolleys and stationary robots is the best bet for most applications.

CHAPTER THIRTEEN

Product design for robot manufacture

SO competitive is business these days, that 'ease of manufacture' is a top design priority; the byways are littered with good designs that either could not be made easily enough for the manufacturer to sell them profitably, or which could not be made to high enough quality standards. Then, there are indifferent products which have been successful largely because they were easy to produce at low cost.

One problem with 'flexible manufacture' is that designers are apt to think that the equipment can handle everything. For example, in one case where a flexible machining system was to be installed, the designers made a number of changes to the products, and omitted to tell the production engineering department. They reasoned that the flexible machining system would be able to handle the revised workpieces. However, the machines were limited in the size of workpiece they could handle, and the revised workpieces were too big to go on the machines. The result was that instead of a whole family of parts being produced by the flexible system, about 30% had to be produced elsewhere. Similar mistakes can easily be made with robots.

Partly because many products to be made by robots were not designed for automation, and partly owing to the way the robot operates, care is needed in design. The principles are not much different from those needed for hard automation, except that it is no longer necessary to divide the operations into cycles of equal length – a line or cell system can be used. On the other hand, experience shows that minor changes in design can make big improvements, and that in almost every case, more care is needed – with jigging, tolerances of parts, the consistency of the viscosity of liquids and so on.

In spot welding, for example, it was found early on that wider flanges were needed – they were increased from about 15 to 18mm. This was not because the robot could not weld accurately, but because the welding fixtures did not hold the bodies precisely enough. Of course, there is a fixture at every station, and the tolerances on manufacture of the fixture led to a larger than expected variation. The lesson is that wherever robots are used, the fixtures must be designed to locate the parts precisely, and the parts should be designed for precise location.

Spot welded parts usually have some inaccessible areas where some spots must be made, and the longer the stretch of the robot, the greater the inaccuracy of positioning. Where possible, the use of welding guns with long jaws should be avoided, as these must be wielded by big and expensive robots. Then, since the whole idea of using robots for spot welding is to run several different products down one line, the clamps needed for the different products should be identical where possible, and well spaced out where they are different. If the various sub-assemblies can be designed so that they naturally hang together more simple jigs can be used. For example, Fiat bodies are held together by interlocking tabs prior to welding, while in some other designs the side assemblies are designed to sit on the underbody so that they are supported naturally.

Because arc welding involves small batches, the minimum of jigging is preferable, which implies that the assemblies should fit together. Where special jigs are used, great care is needed with very thin panels, because they tend to distort during welding. A welder can compensate for this, usually by a deft blow with a hammer, but the robot does not know what is happening. So the two panels may nestle closely together at the beginning of the weld, but by the end of the weld they may be separated by a gap at the other end – and either the gun will not make a weld, or it is likely to burn through. Of course, this problem does not occur with very thick plate, nor in short welds, so one solution may be to weld a long run in a number of sections, or to design the assembly on the basis of short welds.

Where parts are to be handled, at diecasting machines, machine tools, or for palletising, the parts should be designed with a relatively strong portion for the robot to grip. In diecasting, the sprue is usually handled, and this can often be thickened up a little with advantage. Of course, if asked to strengthen a part for handling, designers are apt to ask for the gripper to be improved, but this may not be practical. The result may be that the part has to be installed in a special holder during machining, for example, whereas the addition of a thick collar or lugs at one end, subsequently machined off, may have solved the problem much more cheaply.

For assembly, a major redesign may make the difference between parts that can be assembled by robot, and those that cannot; almost invariably, teams designing robot assembly systems find that with a minor redesign, the job is simplified greatly. For example, in a project to assemble electric motors by robot at the National Engineering Laboratory, at East Kilbride, Scotland, it was necessary to handle loose wires, and to insert a protective rubber grommet around the main supply cable. These are difficult jobs for the robot, but it was found that with minor changes, the capacitor could be supplied as part of a pre-assembly on the stator, so that the loose wires did not need to be handled. Then, by taking the supply cable through a slot in the non-drive end shield, the need for a grommet was eliminated. In addition, the extra slots could be used to orientate the shield. Of course, in every assembly there are many non-critical areas where the design can be improved to ease production.

Electrical relays and vehicle instruments are traditionally assembled manually, but after being redesigned, they are being assembled automatically. Traditionally, relays are rectangular, with parts assembled from the sides and both ends. When redesigned by Nippondenso, the parts were cylindrical, composed of two sub-assemblies – the steel case, which is cup-shape, containing the coil and plunger, and the plastics base with the terminals and contact points. Since all the parts could be assembled from above the sub-assembly, automation could be used. A subsidiary effect of the redesign was that about 114 different types, produced on ten assembly lines was reduced to eight, produced on one line. In fact, they are not assembled by robot, but they could be, with a rather longer cycle time.

But what about those products requiring a lot of dexterity, and assembly of parts from different angles? For example, there are often cases where a couple of levers have to be inserted between a pair of flanges, and then mounted on a spindle. In some cases, springs, washers and even cotter pins are added. The actual operations are simple enough but a lot of dexterity is needed to put them together.

If the housing were to be split into two parts, and one half mounted on its side, the spindle could be inserted easily by robot, and the levers and spring could be added, even though an operator might have to hook the other end of the spring around a peg afterwards. Then, the robot could fit the second half of the housing – in fact it could be a small bracket, not necessarily the complete half-housing – the whole housing could be turned through 90°, fastened together and a spring pin inserted in the spindle. In this case, the two halves of the housing could be bolted or welded together since the object of splitting them was to facilitate production; in service, the assembly could be removed easily enough manually. Of course, when robots are being used in the service department, the story will be different. There are hundreds of similar examples where robot assembly does not seem feasible, because the parts were designed for manual assembly.

On the other hand, that sound design maxim 'keep it simple, stupid' which is essential with manual assembly, is not relevant in all robot assembly jobs. So long as the parts are available, the robot can pick 20 different ones from bowls or feeders and assemble them in the correct sequence every time. Therefore, it may be possible in some cases to break an assembly down into several parts to faciliate some aspect of production. Generally, a robot assembles parts by stacking them one on top of another, and they should be parts that can be fed from vibratory bowls or other parts feeding devices without tangling. Where very delicate parts, such as some wires, have to be assembled, it should be arranged that this can be done at the beginning or end of the robot section – manually. Frequently, for assembly by stacking, the parts feeder must supply a part correctly orientated, and for this purpose, some features, such as a lug or slots are essential.

But what can be done with really complicated assemblies, such as cars, furniture, or even buildings, which do not lend themselves to robot assembly? The trend with car assembly is to do more work off the main line, where access is good. On a sub-line there are many jobs that can be done by robot. With a modular design that would allow the designers to produce models with many varieties of fascia options. Most of the assemblies such as instruments, glove locker and audio units could be installed, and the fasteners tightened by robots. Then, if a fixture is used, many of the mechanical units, such as the engine, transmission and suspension arms can be brought together by robots. Currently, this would seem a very complex fixture and robot, but with system design it is possible.

If the floor is built separately from the body, then first the body shell could be painted completely by robot, and then nearly all the parts could be assembled by being deposited on the floor and fastened as necessary – sound deadening material, carpets, handbrake, pedal box, fascia and seats. Even the rear suspension and fuel tank could be fitted beneath the floor, and later on the spare wheel could be mounted on the boot floor – all by robot. Robots are used by some auto companies to install the spare wheel into the boot, but the rather complex operation would be much simpler if it were mounted on the bare underbody. Once this construction is adopted, the opportunities for using robots increase immeasurably. Of course, there are many jobs where the amount of dexterity needed makes a robot unsuitable, but that is no reason why the car, or any other major assembly should not be designed for robot assembly.

Although components are inserted in printed circuit boards largely by NC machine, the computer, computer peripheral and other electronics assemblies are in need of new thinking before robots can be used widely. Yet these are usually assemblies of parallel boards slid into housings, which should be simple to assemble.

Building is a business that seems totally unsuitable for robots, and of course the first essential is that modules be built in factories, and assembled on site. But some work at Waseda University, under the direction of Professor Yukio Hasegawa, has shown that with a new concept, concrete buildings could be assembled by robots. It is envisaged that the steel bars be formed directly from CAD data, and then the main walls assembled in a factory. There, robots would assemble the mesh of steel bars prior to casting of the concrete panels. To install the concrete walls, a crane would be needed, but this would be unmanned. Instead, an operator would control a manipulator attached to the panel, and the crane would provide servo assistance. With a similarly unfettered approach, many other assemblies can be redesigned to suit robot manufacture, and in most cases, the robot technology is already available. (Fig. 13.1)

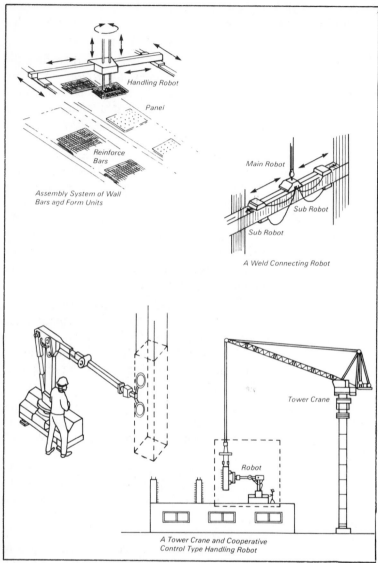

Handling Robot

Panel

Reinforce Bars

Assembly System of Wall Bars and Form Units

Main Robot

Sub Robot

Sub Robot

A Weld Connecting Robot

Tower Crane

Robot

A Tower Crane and Cooperative Control Type Handling Robot

Fig 13.1   With the trend towards new thinking, concrete buildings can be manufactured and assembled with the aid of robots

CHAPTER FOURTEEN
Safety

ROBOTS are powerful and dangerous beasts, and need to be treated as such. Already, at least one man has died in an accident involving a robot, and unless care is taken, more injuries will follow as the use of robots proliferates. Training is equally as important as the guards and sub-systems used in avoiding accidents. The basic principle, of course, is that robots should be kept in areas where operators do not need to go, and where they cannot normally go. That is much easier to arrange in some installations than others, and in any case, maintenance staff must go into the robot area.

In high-volume spot welding lines, safety is a matter of enclosing the robot lines with fences. To open an access gate the operator should be obliged to actuate a switch that shuts down the line, and use a special key. If any gate is opened, the line should shut down anyway. Some companies like to fit flashing beacons in the area, and sound horns at the start of each operation, but workers soon get accustomed to the noise.

It is far more difficult to decide on what is the correct safety level in moulding and machine shops and in assembly. When a robot was installed in a plastics moulding shop in the north of England to unload from a large machine a few years ago, the Factory Inspectorate requested so many precautions that the economics were jeopardised. In addition to the usual fencing and safety switches, the inspector insisted that a device to shut the machine down if anyone tried to enter through the hole where mouldings were discharged should be fitted. That hole was only about 600mm square.

At the other extreme, in one machine shop, operators move about in the robot area, loading buffer stores and removing bins full of machined components. In that case, the areas are

*Fig 14.1   Robot lines need to be fully enclosed by fences, with
interlocks on the gates*

*Fig 14.2   The control system, like this one for KUKA robots, should be
designed with safety in mind*

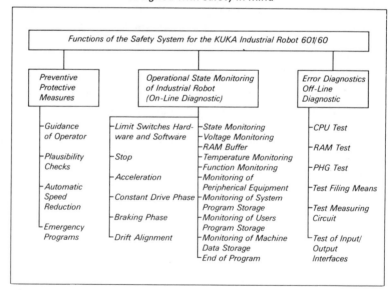

cordoned off with a slim cord at head height, while very small signs indicate that this is a prohibited area. In machining cells, the robot area must be fenced off, and the operator/machine interface must be at the edge of the cell, preferably well distant from the robot.

This is one advantage of the oval carousel store, which can be loaded at the end remote from the robot picking area. Nevertheless, an operator can run in to the area to try to solve a problem with such enthusiasm that he forgets safety. That was evidently what happened in the fatal accident in Japan, and the control system was such that the workers outside the cell could do nothing when the robot struck the man. The lesson from that experience is that operators need regular training, and that there should be plenty of emergency buttons so that people outside the cell can stop the robot moving.

However great the precautions, maintenance staff must get near the robot which needs to be designed to prevent the operator inputting incorrect data and so triggering off unexpected movements. For example, the control system should be such that when setting the robot up to do a certain job, the operator should not be able to operate the robot quickly – 10% of the maximum speed is a suitable limit. The control system should also guide the operator in reprogramming, to prevent him making errors. Equally, the system needs to be designed so that in the event of a failure, the robot will not make unexpected movements. Also, of course, the emergency stop button should be the biggest and easiest button to use on the teachbox.

But what if the robot does strike someone? If the gripper strikes anything, it should stop the robot. In addition, safety rails can be fitted along the body of the robot. The rail is supported on struts about 100mm from the robot body. In the event of the rail striking an object, the whole stops, virtually instantly. Another sensible safeguard found on some machines is that when the operator is in the cage with the robots, he can only programme one at a time. These safeguards may seem a big burden for the robot manufacturer, but if the five or six axes of movement of a robot are suddenly actuated in an unexpected way, the result is likely to be havoc.

In arc welding, the turntable system ensures a reasonable safety standard, in that the operator and robot are normally separated by the table; it is a fairly simple matter to fence off the access to the robot at the sides of the table. Even without a turn-table, the robot and operator are normally separated by the fixture, so the robot should not be a danger. Secondary safety devices are necessary, though, and a pressure sensitive mat, which will shut down the robots if anyone treads on it, is one effective device. This is particularly useful where the workpieces enter a prohibited area.

Assembly seems very difficult, in that to start using robots, companies will want to install a few on an existing line. However, since assembly robots are usually small and not powerful, it is normally easy to enclose them fully in plastics shields; if the shield is removed, of course, the robot should stop moving. With a cell concept, the robots, equipment and con-trollers can be grouped in such a way that the minimum of fencing is needed. Of course with a completely unmanned line, the situation improves immeasurably.

In all these situations, the danger must be recognised, and a balance between safety and commonsense struck; the principle that people should not be able to enter the robot area must be observed, and safety mats and special locks certainly help turn the principle into a reality. If people do circumvent one safety system – and the reason is usually enthusiasm, not mischief – there should be another one. In calculating the real cost of a robot, and the time taken to install one and get it running efficiently, the safety equipment and training must be taken into account.

CHAPTER FIFTEEN

Flexible manufacturing systems (FMS)

FLEXIBILITY has become a key word in manufacture, and now the trend is towards FMS – flexible manufacturing systems. These are designed to produce a variety of products from standard machinery with the minimum of manning levels. In the ultimate system, raw material in the form of bars, plates and powder would be used to produce any assembly required without manual intervention in manufacture. Clearly, a good breeding ground for robots.

But it should be emphasised that the early FMS are really DNC – direct numerical control – systems for machining. And it must be acknowledged that an NC machine tool is really a special-purpose robot. It manipulates a tool in much the same way as a robot handles a tool or welding gun. Then, with no more than a change in programming, it can produce a wide range of products. Added to which, the controllers for robots and NC machines are almost the same. But for an NC machine to be converted into a self-supporting system, it needs some extra equipment, including a handling device, and with these, it forms an important element in FMS.

The principle of FMS for machining is that the NC machines are equipped with monitors for tool wear and tool breakage. Such cells are able to operate unmanned so long as they can be loaded by robot or similar device, since the monitors will detect any fault and shut the machine down. The requirements can be summarised as:

● CNC system with sufficient memory to store many different machining programs;
● Automatic handling at the machine tool – either by robot or some other device;

● Workpiece storage near the machine to allow unmanned operation for several hours;
● A device to monitor wear or any malfunction.

The monitoring device is generally based on a system of measuring the electric current at the main spindle of the machine, and a memory in which data of the normal current are stored, together with data on acceptable limits for operation is incorporated. When the tool wears, the tool changer is actuated, and if the current rises significantly, indicating a tool breakage, the machine is stopped. Thus, with the combination of NC machine, parts store, handling device and monitor, the unmanned cell becomes a reality. Since the control systems of NC machines, robots and unmanned trolleys are similar, central computer control can be used effectively.

Systems based on these principles have been developed by three companies in Japan – Fanuc, the maker of numerical controllers, small NC and EDM machines and robots; Murata, the maker of Robotrailers in Japan, as well as a variety of machinery including textile equipment; and Yamazaki, a large maker of NC machines. In France, Renault and Citroen are also using FMS to machine gearboxes for commercial vehicles, and prototype engine components respectively, while smaller systems have been set up in many other countries.

Fanuc is using a wide range of NC machines, from small lathes to big portal machining centres to produce a wide variety of parts for machine tools and robots. Murata has a system which started off with only seven machining centres producing parts from approximately 1m × 0.5m downwards. Then, Yamazaki has produced a system based on two lines to produce large parts of machine tools. In all cases, there is a hierarchical computer system. The common elements of all these systems are computer control, CNC machining centres, automatic pallet handlers, unmanned trolleys, some buffer storage and computer control. The machine shops are manned for one or two shifts, and unmanned for at least the third shift.

In the Fanuc factory, built specially for the FMS, there are two high-rise automatic warehouses with random access for materials. The one for raw materials and partly-machined workpieces can hold up to 477 workpieces of 1,000 kg, although of course smaller parts can be grouped together in one bin. The other can hold up to 4,000 machined parts.

In the machine shop are 23 CNC machining centres of various sizes and seven CNC lathes. Positioned at each lathe, and at one small CNC machining centre there is a Fanuc robot loading and unloading the machine tool. Each robot works in conjunction with a carousel table, which is indexed around in sequence with the operation of the machine, so that a fresh workpiece is in position for the robot to pick up. These carousels generally carry enough parts for about eight hours operation.

The large CNC machines are served by pallet changers carrying two, four or six workpieces, according to the size of the workpiece and the length of the cycle. The machining cycle for the large parts is usually between two and three hours. Overall, Fanuc is machining 250 different components.

To transfer the workpieces from the store to the machines, and from the machines through inspection to the finished parts warehouse, Digitron-Murata Robotrailers are used. These follow wires buried in the floor. Between the row of machines and the aisle, and near the inspection area is a row of rails to carry workpieces as buffer stock. Each trolley incorporates its own jacking system, and can pick up and deposit workpieces at the buffer stores.

During the day shift, there are 15 people working in the machine shop, and another four in inspection. Before the men go home at the end of their shift, they load up all the pallet changers and carousels for the robots. Then, for the remaining 16 hours of the day, the machine shop operates under the supervision of one man sitting in the separate computer control centre. In addition to all this data, the supervisor has a number of tv monitors which can be linked to the monitor cameras at each of the larger machines.

Since it is not practical to load all the machines with enough pallet changers for 16 hours unmanned operation, some machines work for only 15 hours a day, and others for the full 24. This balance changes according to the products being machined.

Yamazaki's FMS is designed to handle 74 different parts at a rate of 1,450 a month. There are two lines of NC machining centres, the 'A' line consisting of eight horizontal spindle machines handling 23 types of headstocks at a rate of 800 a month. The 'B' line consists of seven vertical and three horizontal spindle machines, arranged to handle the large machine beds, bases and saddles. Production volume is 650 a month, and there are 50 varieties. Since these are large components, the process times – waiting plus machining time – vary from five hours to three days on the B line, whereas the headstocks are processed in five to 24 hours on the A line.

The lines are installed in parallel, each being about 100m long, with rails for the unmanned trolleys alongside each. At one end of the shop, the four operators load workpieces on pallets. At the other end are the tool room and computer room, one man working in each. The unmanned trolleys run from the set-up area to the other end of the shop, passing between the pallet changers at the machines and a row of buffer storage stations. Only three days' production is needed as work-in-progress for the whole system, against 90 days' work-in-progress with conventional operation, the company claims.

Each machine on the A line is equipped, unusually, with two tool drums mounted back to back on a column. An automatic travelling crane – called a robot by Yamazaki, since it works in response to computer control – transports the column/tool drum assemblies to the tool room as necessary to be exchanged for assemblies carrying different tools.

The operators working on the two shifts arrange workpieces on the pallets, which are then transported to the buffer area or direct to the pallet changers. They also unload machined workpieces from the pallets for onward transport to assembly. During the two manned shifts, sufficient stock is built up in the buffer line to keep the machines working throughout the third shift. In the third shift, the trolley moves the workpieces between the pallet changers and buffer line only, a function it also performs in the manned shifts. Yamazaki has also built a larger FMS with 65 machines and 34 robots to produce smaller parts. Grinding and heat treatment equipment are included as well as machining centres and CNC lathes. The productivity per man will be ten times that of conventional machine tool manufacturers, the company claims.

Murata's system is altogether smaller and simpler, with seven machining centres initially, three more having been installed subsequently. There was one row of four OKK vertical spindle machines, and another of three Yasuda horizontal spindle machines, and adjacent is the set-up area and automatic storage system. Running between the machining centres, the stores and the set-up area are two Robotrailers which follow cables buried in the floor.

In the warehouse are 220 bays – enough for two days' operation – and so that the men can book goods in and out, the computer terminal is near the setting area. Automatically, the stacker crane, which can carry two pallets/workpiece assemblies at a time, brings down new workpieces and the appropriate fixtures to the bays, where the men set the workpieces on the fixtures and pallets. The complete assembly then goes back into the stores.

Meanwhile, the stacker crane withdraws workpiece/pallet assemblies from the stores and places them on a loading platform. The Robotrailer is then instructed to take the workpiece to a certain machine. Each machine is equipped with a two-station automatic pallet changer, on to which the Robotrailer slides the pallet. When the workpiece is finished, the Robotrailer removes it from the automatic pallet changer and takes it to the setting area. There, it is removed from the pallet, and placed on a wooden pallet to be returned to the stores. Thus, the operators need only load and unload the pallets, all other operations, including handling and control being automatic.

In the Renault FMS, five CNC machining centres are combined with eight unmanned trolleys to provide a set-up to machine cast iron and aluminium gearbox housings for trucks. The machines are suitable for housings of up to a 600mm cube, and the initial production rate was 70 units a day, the plant operating on three shifts. Output was due to be increased to 100 a day soon afterwards.

Citroen installed three CNC machining centres to machine prototype batches of engine cylinder heads, gearbox casings and other housings. In this case, the workpieces were limited to a 500mm cube, and they are carried on 800mm square pallets.

A computer controlled co-ordinate measuring sytem and washing machine were also included in the system, which is served by five unmanned trolleys. There is a central parts store, with a capacity of 54 parts, and a central tool store with 600 tools. In this case, up to 60 tools can be used on any workpiece, and the minimum cycle time for economic operation is 10 min. The machines are operated for 24 h daily under control of the computer system.

All these systems have produced impressive results in productivity and profits. Fanuc claims that the productivity/ investment ratio has been increased by 1.5 times, while productivity/worker has increased five times.

Yamazaki puts its investment at £9 million against £7 million for a normal NC plant, and potential sales output at £14 million a year against £11 million. However, because total work-in-progress of the conventional shop is valued at £2,500,000 against £120,000 for FMS, the profitability of the two plants is completely different. Then, labour costs of the FMS are much lower, with 12 people instead of 70. Thus, the payback period is two and a half years, and Yamazaki calculates that over a five year period, the FMS will pay for itself and produce a surplus of £13 million, whereas a conventional NC plant would only just get into the black by £1 million.

Murata Machinery claims that its system has quadrupled the return on investment, and its records show that it has cut downtime from 35 to 7.5%. The impressive feature of this system is that it involved an investment of only about £400,000, and that it has been installed in an existing machine shop. The return on investment of a complete set-up, including NC machines, is 4.2 times that of a normal NC shop. One reason is the big cut in downtime, and another is that the manning level is down from 20 to six.

Renault invested £4 million in its FMS, which is operated by a total of 15 people. Because set-up time is eliminated, much higher machine utilisation than normal is obtained, while operating costs are lower. Citroen spent £3,200,000, of which £2,100,000 was required for the machines, the remaining for engineering. It claimed that a normal system would have cost £3,500,000 and would have needed 73 operators. As it is, 33 people are needed for the complete FMS. These are: direct labour, first shift 5, second shift 4, night shift, none. Surveillance, one man on each shift; there are also one controller and two maintenance men on each day shift. Thus, a total of 18 men work in the shop. In addition, another 15 men, including 10 programmers and one supervisor, are needed to operate the system. However, when other FMS are installed, the overhead of the programmers should be reduced, but in any case, the total manning level is well below 50% of that for a conventional machine shop.

Other than unmanned trolleys, there are not many robots in these systems, mainly because the cycle times are long, and it easier to establish an FMS with long than with short cycles. But as FMS with shorter cycles are installed so the use of robots will proliferate – indeed, they are the way to obtain low manning levels and short cycles with FMS.

The key to these gains is in the unmanned operation at night, and the fact that the plant can run for 24 hours. Clearly, these are the forerunners of a whole new concept in manufacture. In due course it will be possible to run for two shifts with only one computer operator, and perhaps by 1990, this job will be done by an intelligent robot. But quite soon it should be possible to expand the control and handling system so that if a tool is worn or damaged, it is changed automatically and work can proceed, even if the cell is unmanned.

In due course, this concept will spread to assembly and inspection, and already some companies are operating assembly robots for 24 hours a day, although the operators work for only one shift. Then, the Japanese government, through its Agency for Industrial Science and Technology (AIST) is sponsoring a project for a completely flexible manufacturing system. The idea is that with standard tooling, powder metallurgy parts and forgings can be produced. Then, they will be machined on a number of special NC machines, assembled on some assembly robots, and finally inspected automatically. A central laser, directing its beam through conduits will be used for heat treatment and welding. In this way, a manufacturing system, capable of producing any type of gear or shaft housing weighing 20–30 kg could be produced.

This particular scheme looks altogether too complicated to be practical, but the message is clear: by 1990, many products will be made with very low manning levels, and computer-controlled robot systems will play an important part in that major change in manufacture, with real FMS being in wide use for forming, machining and assembly. (Fig. 15.1)

Significantly, to give a reasonable return on capital, these plants will need to operate 24 hours a day. Therefore, either they will be very small, or output will magnify enormously, yet manning levels will be reduced to a fraction of what they are today. Since they will be able to operate very flexibly, they would seem to leave little scope for the very small workshop. In fact, the reverse is likely to be true. Since these plants will have high overheads, the small one-to-five man operation will be able to compete effectively, especially if it takes advantage of the same combination of robots and ancillary equipment as the larger companies; only the scale need differ.

For example, it will be quite feasible for one man to design products with the aid of CAD/CAM, order the materials, and set up his tiny machine shop to make them without leaving his desk. Someone will need to feed the materials in somewhere, of course, but one man will be able to handle far more aspects of a job than at present. Then, one man might run an automated plastics moulding shop, and need to go there only once or twice a day. In between, he could deliver mouldings, seek new orders and take time off. Clearly, a new era in manufacture has arrived.

Fig 15.1   Control and supervision architecture for an FMS

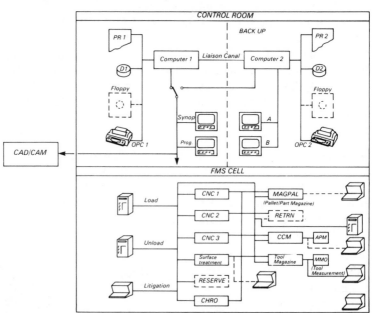

CHAPTER SIXTEEN
Where are robots taking us?

IN the short term, there is no doubt that the growth rate for robot production and use will be spectacular, particularly as most economic modellers talk of 30–50% growth annually until the mid 1980s.

In 1981, there were about than 20,000 real robots in the world, with roughly 9,000 in Japan, 4,000 in the USA and 5,000 in Europe. By 1985, there are likely to be over 70,000 robots in the world. These figures are only approximations, but they do show that if industry is considered as a whole, the robot population will not be large. After all, there are already far more than 100,000 automation devices in use now.

However, in the next five years, the types of robots will proliferate. For example, at present, some of the large robot manufacturers only produce two or three basic models, which are usually classified by weight capacity – one might have a capacity of 5kg, and the other 30kg; in another company, the models are 6 and 60kg.

In the next few years, as the market expands we can expect to see many more in-between models in both reach and lifting capacity. Then, there will be special long-reach models, and devices that will not look like robots at all. In other words, the robot will change from being a clearly discernible device that is like a humanoid manipulator to an ordinary machine.

Some will look like manipulators, others will look like hard automation, and others will be hidden in complex process plant and equipment. In other cases, robots will be integrated with bowl feeders and conveyors to provide automated systems.

Of course, there will be some robots that will move around on wheels, and others that will walk – mainly for use on the

Fig 16.1   One view of the robot future that has little relevance to
manufacturing industry

ocean bed where there is a whole new world waiting for successful but costly robots. However, the concept of the robot getting
more human-like in appearance and 'intelligence' is wide of the
mark. Sensing will make big strides forward in vision and touch,
while there will be multiple armed robots, some of which will be
extremely dexterous. But what is needed most from robotics are
devices to improve manufacture, and to eliminate dirty and
heavy jobs. Within five years it should not be necessary for a
man to fettle castings, expose himself to the heat of a furnace,
pour molten iron or move anywhere near a nuclear hazard.

These changes will come about both under pressure from
users who will find better ways of applying robots as well as the
need for more specific designs. For example, most surveys show
that at present robots are reprogrammed on average no more
than once a week, and that volumes are often 50,000–100,000 a
year, with batches of around 1,000. In due course, robots that
can be programmed for any process in a few seconds will be
available, so that they will be suitable for batches of one to 100
with short cycle times. It is when that happens that the real
explosion in robot use will take place – so long as companies
and workers are ready to exploit the situation. (Figs. 16.1, 16.2)

Superimposed on these visual changes will be a number of
invisible ones. For example, controllers will have much larger

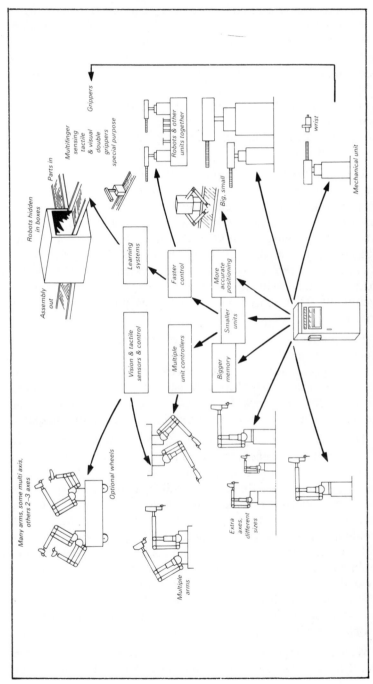

Fig 16.2 Directions in which robots are likely to develop

memories, and will be able to control more axes than now, as well as peripheral equipment including sensors. In addition, there will be a gradual switch from dc to ac servo motors. The ac motors currently require complicated and expensive electronics, but the motor itself has no brushes, and is much simpler and smaller. It will be practical to fit these motors inside arms, instead of sticking them on the outside like warts, as is the practice now. As the cost of electronics falls, so ac servo motors will come into use, hopefully reducing overall cost and improving reliability.

Tactile gripping and compliance are features that will broaden the robot's ability in handling and assembly immensely. Vision is needed, too, but in many cases as a supervisory device to check that the robots are doing all the jobs they should, and that parts are available. Thus, it is quite likely that in most cases, the robot and vision system will remain separate units. Among the exceptions is arc welding, where a vision system that can see the weldpath while welding is going on must arrive on the scene eventually. That sensor will probably be placed on the robot arm.

The immediate effect of the proliferation of robots will be much higher levels of automation in big volume industries such as cars, consumer durables and electronics products. These companies will widen their product ranges, and will obsolete models even more quickly than now, as they see the robot giving them the ability to respond to marketing changes more quickly.

This mad charge to plug every gap in the market irrespective of whether it is of benefit to the consumer or declared objectives in conservation of materials is already evident in Japan. The one useful by-product of this change will be that less scrap will be produced, which to some extent will counter this potential squandering of resources. But it is doubtful whether the proliferation in variety of products will be beneficial to mankind, and it is certainly a duty of governments and engineers to try to avoid unnecessary waste. But each company has to survive, and it can do that only by remaining competitive. However, there are different ways of being competitive, and in general robots give more chance for flexibility than any other device – whether in a flexible manufacturing system or not.

Whichever way this robot revolution goes, we can be sure that there will be less need for unskilled labour than at present, but that there will be a far greater need for skilled labour – from mechanical and electronics designers to maintenance engineers capable of dealing with electronics and mechanisms. Indeed, most surveys carried out into the future growth of the robot business expect that a lack of knowledge, both about robots generally, and how to engineer installations and maintain the machines will restrict the growth of robot usage.

But how do the trades unions see the robot? In Japan, the unions, which are generally powerless, have accepted them from the start, mainly because they have been installed by large companies which guarantee their workers employment till retirement. Therefore, there is no reason for them to object. However, Sohyo, the confederation of unions in the public services, has warned that micro-electronics generally will harm employment opportunities. In Denmark, the unions have won an agreement that no new technology will be introduced without consultation. In the UK, many union leaders seem to accept that robots are necessary, and no troubles were encountered in companies that installed robots in the late 1970s and early 1980s. In all these cases, though, the management took pains to consult the workforce first.

The general view of the IMF, the federation of unions involved principally in engineering, is that robots will improve working conditions, by taking over dirty, heavy and repetitive jobs. They also hope that living standards will rise as robots are introduced. But on the other hand, they are concerned about loss of jobs, and realise that even if the automotive industry in the USA increases output significantly over the next decade, no new jobs will be created. They are also worried because the robot explosion started in a recession, and fear that the growth in the use of robots will erode union power, as plants become smaller.

As a counter to this, the need for more skilled workers is welcomed. Herman Rebhan, the IMF general secretary, thinks that the robot revolution will lead people to spend less time at work. He believes the whole idea of work needs to be rethought; that employees of all levels should be sent on education courses by their employers, and that the shorter working week is desirable. Certainly, we are now at a time when the concept of work needs to be thought about. People need to be motivated to work more conscientiously than ever, yet eventually may need to work far less hours each week. These people will need to be more imaginative in the way they think at work.

In fact, the effect of robots themselves on employment levels are certainly exaggerated. For example, in a nationwide manufacturing industry employing 10 million people, an increase in robot population from 300 to 5,000 will have a negligible effect on employment, so long as there is a commitment among management and employees to remain competitive. As the recession has shown, companies that allow themselves to become uncompetitive are suffering much more, and much more quickly than they used to. If each manufacturing company can generate an average of just 1% growth a year, then an extra 10,000 people per million employees will be needed. Thus, with an industry employing 10 million people, 100,000 people or about 50,000 robots are needed to increase output by 1%.

Clearly, a country the size of Britain is unlikely to be able to install 200,000 robots in the next few years – 1,000 a year is probably more likely. Thus, in the short term, the effect on employment levels as a whole will be negligible. If a good proportion of those robots are made where they are used, then their effect on employment will be less. But the pattern of where the unemployment crops up will present government and people with major problems – especially where there is no real commitment to remaining competitive.

It is equally clear that the nature of employment will change. Whether office workers will actually work at home in large number, as forecast by some futurologists, is by no means certain. People will actually do less with their hands than at present.

Forging and machining will be automatic, robots will do almost all handling, and will do assembly, while special tools with some robotic features will spread to the service industries. All this means that people will spend more time watching things, or checking on operations without actually doing them. This will also be true of engineers and designers who will work with CAD/CAM systems.

If the robotic revolution can be used to increase economic growth, then people will have the time and income to enjoy more leisure or more leisurely work. The three-day week, in which the four holidays a week are well paid, has long seemed a dream. But it will be worth having only if the output per machine is increased dramatically. Otherwise, the three-day week will

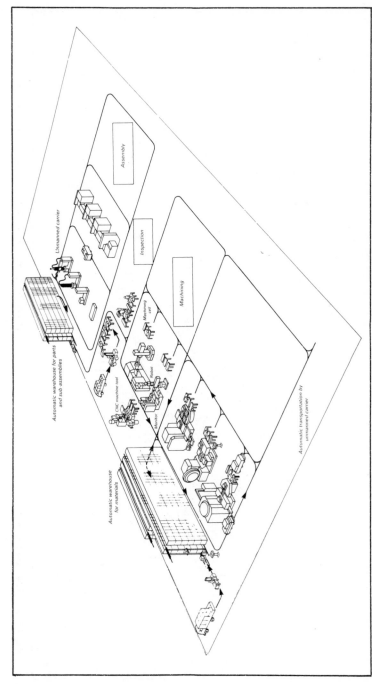

Fig 16.3   With the aid of robot trolleys and robot handling at NC machines, machine shops can run unmanned

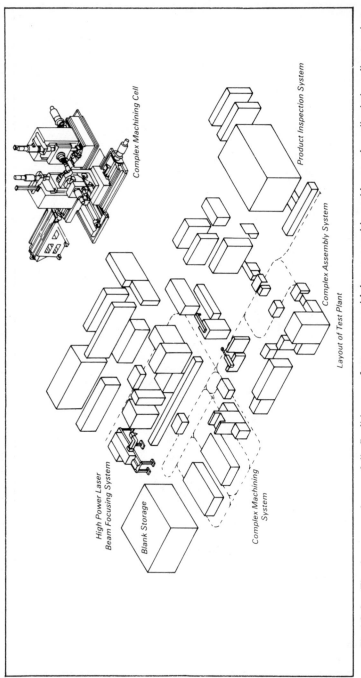

Fig 16.4   The Japanese view on fully flexible manufacture – machining, assembly and inspection all rely heavily on robot handling

materialise, but not with the necessary living standard to go with it.

With more time on our hands, and higher incomes, there will be a temptation to buy more useless things, and certainly a host of unthought-of products, some useful and others useless will come with developments in microelectronics and robots. Many manufacturers will produce more and more variations on products with short lives in the hope of remaining profitable. So there is a real danger that we shall end up squandering our resources, producing more and more useless products, that people will buy only because they have sufficient money to do so. To avoid that problem, a sound education is the best base; indeed, whichever way you look at robots, the biggest challenge they pose is to education. First, it will be necessary to educate engineers and managers how to make the most of robots; secondly, it will be necessary to upgrade the technical skills of engineering workers. Then, people must be encouraged to think more postively and expansively about work, and to understand the value of the resources we have. All that, of course, is on top of the need to educate children to cope with these things as well as the forthcoming knowledge-intensive world.

Bibliography and References

General
Robotics Bibliography 1970–1981, IFS (Publications), 1982
Industrial Robots, Vol. 1: Fundamentals; Vol 2 Applications; Society of Manufacturing Engineers, 1981
Industrial Robots: Application Experience, Publisher Prof. Dr.-Ing. H-J Warnecke, IPA, Stuttgart.
Proc. 11th International Symposium on Industrial Robots, (11th ISIR), Tokyo, October 1981.
Proceedings of Robots in the Automotive Industry, (RAI), Birmingham, April 1982.

References
Chapter 1
Present situations and future demands for some industrial robots, Kanji Yonemoto et al, page 25; 11th ISIR.
Chapter 5
Robotic Welding of 'S' truck at GMC truck and coach, R. E. Berg and J. D. Lane, pages 59–74; Proc: Robots in the Automotive Industry, (RAI) Birmingham UK
Robots enter Ford truck manufacturing, S. L. Roswell, pages 95–106; Proc: RAI.
Present and future applications of industrial robots in the automotive industry, S. Muller, pages 205–217; Proc: RAI.
Mix the models when robots do the welding, *The Engineer*, 20 July, 1978.
Small and fast, they weld car bodies, *The Engineer*, 5 February, 1981
Chapter 6
A growing family to cut welding drudgery, *The Engineer*, 23 February, 1978.
Letting robots take the strain, *The Engineer*, 18 January, 1979.

A production experiment in cellular manufacture, *Industrial Robot*, June 1981.

Improving quality and productivity in foundries, *Industrial Robot*, March 1982.

Installation and operation of industrial robot experiences by Saab-Scania AB, C. G. Wikholm, pages 173–180; Proc: RAI.

Chapter 7

Home-grown arc welding robots reap dividends, *Industrial Robot*, September 1982.

Arc welding robot with vision, I. Masaki et al; Proc: 11th ISIR, p. 813.

A visual sensor for arc welding robots, T. Bamba et al; Proc: 11th ISIR, p. 151.

Chapter 8

Review of application and operation experience in the automotive industry with the DeVilbiss Trallfa spray painting robot, D. E. Jarvis, pages 1–12; Proc: RAI.

Robot painting, *Electronic Times*, 22 April, 1982.

Assembly and machine loading will dominate General Motors robotics programme, *Industrial Robot*, December 1981.

Chapter 9

The use of the DEA Pragma A3000 robot in the assembly of automotive components, M. A. Badger, pages 149–156; Proc: RAI.

Systems analysis and experimental study advance the art of assembly automation, *Assembly Automation*, August 1981.

Developing assembly robots on the shopfloor, *Assembly Automation*, November 1981.

Flexible unmanned mechanical assembly system with Fanuc Robot A Series, *Robot*, No. 32.

Sankyo articulated assembly robot Skilam, *Robot*, No. 32.

NEL's adaptable robot assembly system, *Assembly Automation*, May 1982.

Chapter 10

Robot control and inspection by multiple camera vision system, A. G. Makhlin, page 121; Proc: 11th ISIR.

Trainable assembly system with an active sensory table possessing six axes, M. Kasai et al, page 393; Proc: 11th ISIR.

Computer assisted vision at Fiat automobile works for assembly of body parts and surface inspection of mechanical components, U. L. Businaro et al, pages 163–172; Proc: RAI.

Robot Vision, edited by Professor Alan Pugh. Published by IFS Publications, UK, and Springer-Verlag, Berlin, 1983.

Proceedings of the 2nd International Conference on Robot Vision and Sensory Controls, Stuttgart, West Germany, 2–4 November 1982. Published by IFS Publications Ltd, UK

Chapter 11

Pilot installations for fettling of castings with industrial robots – basic equipment, strategies, experiments and results, H-J Warnecke et al, page 713; Proc: 11th ISIR.

Robot centres aim to boost customer service, *Industrial Robot*, June 1981.

Measuring in automated manufacturing process, *Sensor Review*, April 1982.

Chapter 12

The human approach which gives Fiat a high-quality engine, *The Engineer*, 5 November, 1981.

Development of guideless robot vehicle, K. Fujiwara et al. page 51; Proc: 11th ISIR.

Chapter 13

Robotization of reinforced concrete building construction, Y. Hasegawa; Proc: 11th ISIR.

Chapter 15

Why Japan is putting more emphasis on FMC projects, *The Engineer*, 20 January, 1981.

Unmanned by night, and manned by day, *The Engineer*, 19 November, 1981.

The little and large ways to flexibility, *The Engineer*, 8/15 April, 1982.

The FMS Report, edited by John Mortimer. Published by IFS Publications Ltd, UK.

Proceedings of the 1st International Conference on Flexible Manufacturing Systems, Brighton, UK, 20–22 October 1982. Published by IFS Publications Ltd, UK

Index